# THE CULBIN S₄
# FACT AND FI(

## Sinclair Ross

**Centre for Scottish Studies**
**University of Aberdeen**

First published 1992

© Sinclair Ross

ISBN 0 906265 16 9

Typeset from author-generated discs
and printed by BPCC-AUP Aberdeen Ltd.

# CONTENTS

# LIST OF PLATES

# LIST OF FIGURES

# LIST OF APPENDICES

For Jean

# AUTHOR'S ACKNOWLEDGEMENTS

I am grateful for assistance from the following sources:
The Forestry Commission for unrestricted access to the Culbin Forest over the years, and for their generous contribution towards the cost of publication.
Sandy Cram and Sandy Watson for discussions on forestry and much encouragement.
Moray District Libraries.
Moray District Record Office.
Kris Sangster for the cover illustration and figure 28.
George Brown for plate 3.
The late David Forrester for plates 4, 14 and 15.
The British Geological Survey for plates 10, 11, 12 and 13.
Cambridge University for plate 19.
The Forestry Commission for plates 16, 17 and 18.
The National Museum of Antiquites for plates 23 and 24.
Messrs Robert Hale Limited for plates 9 and 20, originally reproduced in *The Buried Barony* by A.A. Macgregor.
Messrs Methuen for figure 26.
Borehole data was provided by:
    The Department of the Environment for Kinloss Airfield
    Carol Knight for Findhorn
    United Distilling Cereals Ltd. for Roseisle Maltings
    Moray District Council for Roseisle, Cassieford and Forres
Finally my sincere thanks to John Kinnaird for stimulating discussions on the family history of the Kinnairds and permission to include data from his unpublished resources.

Sinclair Ross
Forres, October 1991

# EDITOR'S PREFACE

Sinclair Ross, an Orcadian, first walked in Culbin in the early 1950s soon after taking up the post of Weather Forecaster at Royal Air Force, Kinloss. His interest in geological matters goes back to a spell in Germany where he purchased a copy of Holmes' *Principles of Physical Geology*. Inspired by that well-loved and influential textbook, Sinclair later undertook a serious study of petrology which he used to good effect in his study of the lava pebbles he discovered in Culbin for which there appeared to be no known outcrops! The search for the origins of these pebbles led him into geomorphological as well as geological matters, and inevitably into the literature and evidence on the ground for the origins of the Culbin Sands. As his curiosity grew, and his observations and mapping multiplied, it became clear to him that the existing literature contradicted the evidence on the ground. This book is the result of these observations, brought together for the first time into a single volume. Short accounts of aspects of the Culbin Story compiled by Sinclair Ross have been published in the past both in *The Moray Book* and in the *Moray Field Club Bulletin*. Sinclair Ross is President of the Highland Geological Club and has led excursions throughout the Highlands, as well as in Lower Moray and the Culbin. In combining meticulous fieldwork with documentary research, and presenting the results in appetising form, Sinclair, as a self-taught geologist follows in the academic footsteps of Hugh Miller, the Cromarty stone mason. Like Hugh Miller, he would be the first to acknowledge the encouragement and help given by many academic geological colleagues. The Centre for Scottish Studies is pleased to be the means of bringing Sinclair's work on Culbin into print. A major re-appraisal on the Culbin story is long overdue.

John S. Smith

# INTRODUCTION

## SYNOPSIS

The Culbin Sands, on the southern shores of the Moray Firth, are today covered by a flourishing forest some 28 square kilometres in extent, but photographs taken there 80 years ago show panoramas of endless sandy wastes with dunes up to 30 metres in height.

The unique development of the area from desert to forest has, over the past 100 years , been studied by specialists from many callings and with the area now designated as a SSSI there are regular visits by groups from universities, learned societies and schools.

The many thousands of artefacts discovered among the dunes indicate that the area has been frequented by man for at least 3500 years and the extent of the desert landscape has led to endless speculation as to its origin. Very little work has been done on the geomorphology of the Culbin Foreland over the past 50 years, and during an investigation into coastal

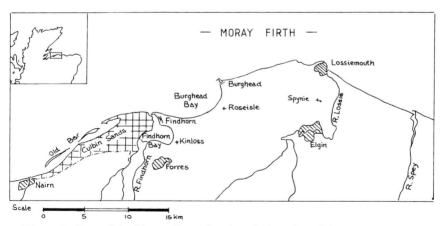

Figure 1    Part of the Moray Coast showing the location of the Culbin Sands.

1

processes involved in its development, a sequence of events has been established linking the westward migration of shingle bars in the longshore drift at the rise of the Post-Glacial Sea with an extensive fluvio-glacial shingle fan at the mouth of the River Spey, 30 kilometres to the east.

Fragmentary evidence regarding the destruction of an estate by the sands in 1694 was woven into a wonderful account of how the Barony of Culbin was engulfed in a single night. The estate, owned by a family of Kinnairds, was said to comprise of 16 farms covering 1456 hectares, while its rents indicated that it was the most fertile in the land. The Laird, with his wife and child, escaped on the night of the storm, only to be hounded to an early grave by his creditors—so both the estate and the family perished: or so it was believed.

In 1867 a local historian published an inaccurate and highly imaginative description of the destruction of the Barony of Culbin, and at the beginning of the present century another local writer produced several embroidered versions of this earlier account. Over the last 100 years many authors have written on various aspects of the Culbin Sands, and, almost without exception have used for the history extracts from these two sources which they have quoted *verbatim* without any further investigation. The continued repetition has led to the widespread acceptance of this version as being the true sequence of events.

Mapping of the shingle ridges which form the backbone of "The Culbin" (as it is known locally), and the extent of the former estuarine soils, which became the agricultural lands of the old estate, has shown that the farm lands could not possibly have been so extensive as the popular accounts suggest. No maps of the Barony of Culbin have survived, but a search for documents linked with the old family produced enough evidence to allow a picture to be built up of both its extent and probable rents, confirming that both had been greatly exaggerated. Additional information and surviving plans from neighbouring estates allowed the boundaries of the Barony of Culbin to be fixed and showed that it covered only 20% of the area given in the legends. The 16 farms were shown to be 16 tenants working 6 holdings, while the original 1456 ha given as the area of the estate proved to be an estimate of the extent of the entire Culbin Sands made some 200 years later.

Taking into account the primitive nature of agriculture in the Highlands and the adverse climatic conditions which had produced periodic famine conditions in Scotland throughout the whole of the 17th century, the much-quoted rental of Culbin for 1693 is thought to have been an attempt at a valuation and not an annual rental. In the final decade of that century there were seven successive years with crop failure and at that time most landowners incurred heavy debts. The Laird of Culbin was but one of many who had to sell his property to pay his creditors and it is only due

Plate 1    The Mouth of the River Spey in 1974, looking west.

to the dramatic legends which have been woven round the Sands that he alone is remembered.

Public records from the period have added details of business deals and family affairs to the history of the Kinnairds of Culbin. This has allowed a much more complete family tree to be established, and members of the family have been traced to much later dates.

More information on the Culbin Sands will no doubt come to light, and while this version of events is not considered to be the definitive account, it is hoped it will go some way towards separating fact from fiction.

## THE CULBIN SANDS TODAY

Along the southern shores of the Moray Firth some 50km of the coastline are formed from unconsolidated sands and shingle of fluvio-glacial origin. The Culbin Sands lie on this coast between the River Findhorn and the River Nairn (fig. 1).

The whole of this stretch is covered by blown sand, with spectacular dunes reaching up to 30m in height. Old photographs show it to have been a desert-like wilderness and there are historical records of severe sandblowing which buried stretches of farmland. Over the past 100 years however, the sands have been stabilised by afforestation, and today the 28 square kms of the Culbin Sands are covered by a thriving forest.

The land surface on which the dunes lie is a low foreland which in the northeastern half consists of a area of estuarine flats enclosed on the seaward side by a large curved stretch of raised beach shingle, the highest part of which reaches 9.0m OD. The southwestern half is a flat, poorly-drained stretch of former saltings, flanked on its landward side by an old fossil cliff line rising to 20–25m OD. Against this bank lies a wet peaty hollow with two shallow lochs at the southwest end. The dunes are largely concentrated in the northeastern half, while towards the southwest, apart from the isolated, blow-out remnants of the large Maviston dunes, they become low and scattered.

This part of the Moray Coast is exposed to any heavy seas coming in from the open northeast quarter, and while gales from this direction are extremely rare, should any on-shore gale coincide with a spring tide, coastal erosion can be severe. Several years may pass with no noticeable effect and then large stretches can be washed away in a single night. In the more active part these losses average 1.5m per annum. Along the northern edge of the Culbin Sands waves can attack a coastline formed only of blown sand without a protecting shingle ridge along high water mark. At the eastern end of this stretch the exit channel from Findhorn

Plate 2    The Old Bar in 1974, looking east.

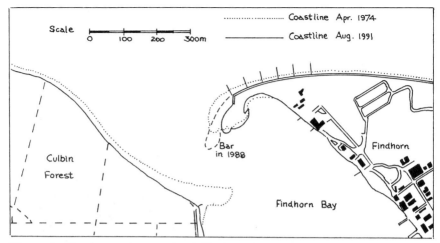

Figure 2   Erosion at the mouth of Findhorn Bay over the last 17 years, 1974–
1991.

Bay, which is tidal, now runs against the Culbin shore and tidal scour has removed 125m from this point in the last 17 years (fig. 2).

Hooked shingle spits build westward across the river mouths on the Moray Coast, with a particularly good example at the mouth of the River Spey (Plate 1). This bar has a good supply of shingle feeding in from the east and it grows westwards at around 40m per year. At the mouth of the Findhorn however, so much shingle has been eroded out of Burghead Bay that it now has a semi-circular shape and only a small amount of shingle feeds west to the present bar at Findhorn. Prior to 1701 there was a very substantial bar across the mouth of Findhorn Bay, and in that year the river broke through the neck of the bar which had been narrowed by erosion. The remains drifted off westward and this portion, known as the Old Bar, through now badly eroded, is still a magnificent sight from the air (Plate 2). The growth of the new bar across the mouth of the Findhorn Bay (Plate 3) is another text-book example of the processes involved in longshore drift, but the building of a series of groynes on the eastern side in 1985 halted its westward growth and the spit is now receding slowly eastwards.

Plate 3  The bar of Findhorn in 1985, looking east, Findhorn Bay to the right, Burghead Bay to the left.

# THE FORM OF CULBIN

## THE FORM OF THE CULBIN FORELAND

Historical accounts and maps of the Culbin area go back over 400 years, and during that period considerable changes in the river channel have occurred and the coastline has been completely altered. Sufficient information is available for us to deduce from the sequence of events a pattern of coastal erosion processes which can be extended farther back in time to establish the probable developments along the Moray Coast since the end of the Ice Age.

A manuscript of a survey of Western Moray by the Rev. Timothy Pont, dating from 1590, is the earliest known detailed map of the area (fig. 3). It shows the River Findhorn flowing westwards along the north side of the Culbin with a long bar on the seaward side. When the map was later published in Blaeu's Moravia in 1654 the bar was not included (Appendix 2). In the 1685 survey for the British Coastal Pilot of 1695, the old village of Findhorn is shown, situated on the bar itself, and the sandhills of Neveston (Maviston) feature as a landmark.

The bar was described as being some 6 miles long, when in 1701, the river breached it close to the present mouth of Findhorn Bay (Grant & Leslie, 1798). Other authors suggest 1702 as the date (Young, 1871), or 1704 (Shaw, 1776), while Ritchie (1932) goes as far as giving Sunday 11th October, 1702 as the date. The river channel had been slowly shallowing due to sand-blowing and the neck of the bar near the village was being eroded, so the inhabitants of the old village of Findhorn, being aware of the potential danger to their homes, had gradually deserted the site and founded a new village some 1.6km to the southeast. The river finally cut through the bar, but by that time all the inhabitants had moved.

A good selection of maps has survived to give us a detailed record of its progress (Appendix 1). A particularly important map is that by Peter May (1758) on which, as well as details of the new river mouth, the old course of the river and the Old Bar are shown (fig. 4). Other maps down to the present day enable us to plot the later movements of the Old Bar (fig. 5). This showed the western end extended southwestwards by 3360m in 232 years, giving an annual rate of 14.5m. In stormy periods the rate can be

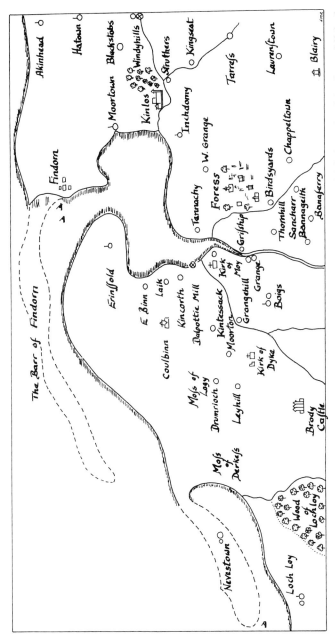

Figure 3  Timothy Pont's manuscript map of Western Moray, 1590. Note the bar which is omitted in the published version.

higher and Steers (1937) and Morrison (1976) note figures of just over 16m per annum over shorter periods.

The severing of the Old Bar in 1701 cut it off from the supply of shingle and its growth from that time onwards has been maintained by the erosion of its eastward half. A map of 1858 showed the Old Bar to be one unit (fig. 6) but since then a small spit has come westwards from the Buckie Loch area and has sheltered the northeast portion of the Old Bar from wave action. This part now remains stationary, while the sea attacks the exposed stretches farther to the southwest and has completely severed the Old Bar. With no fresh shingle coming forward the central portion has been eroded out into a curve, marked by a low pebbly ridge, which has advanced landwards over the saltings by approximately 100m in the past 20 years (figs. 6, 7, 8). Sets of poles which were erected on the flat saltings inside the Old Bar as anti-glider defences during the last war, now stand on the open beach to the seaward of the curve. The remaining part of the bar continues to move towards Nairn and between 1979 and 1991 was losing an average of 2.75m per annum from the shingle ridges along its northeast end.

This process, where a partially sheltered bar continued to extend in the longshore drift and left the saltings open to attack proved to be one of the vital steps in the formation of the original Culbin Foreland.

The changes at the mouth of Findhorn Bay are also of interest, and the same series of maps shows the spit there growing westward at only 2.3m per annum due to the small supply of shingle. Grant and Leslie (1798) describe the shoreline between Findhorn and Burghead prior to 1701 as being "a right line" but the erosion of the neck of the bar at the old village of Findhorn points to an already diminishing supply of shingle due, no doubt, to Burghead Bay already having a deeply curved form. The maps also show that the stretch of coast near Findhorn, which was protected in 1985 by defences costing £3/4 M, was an offshore shingle spit a little over 100 years ago (fig. 9).

Ogilvie (1923) and Steers (1937) studied the geomorphology of the Moray coast and mapped the area before afforestation and airfield construction obscured much of the detail inland. They recognised series of fossil storm beach shingle ridges and spits preserved in the interior of the Culbin and inland from Burghead Bay. The highest of these reached up to about 9.5m O.D. and developed when the sea stood 5.5m above the present level. The very detailed mapping done by Fisher for Steers (1937) agrees closely with later aerial photographs. The western part of the area had already been planted at the time of his mapping, but the present writer found that one

Figure 4    Peter May's map of 1758.

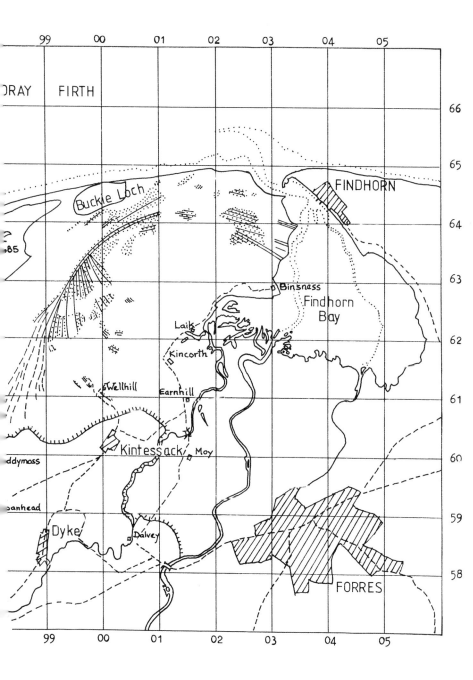

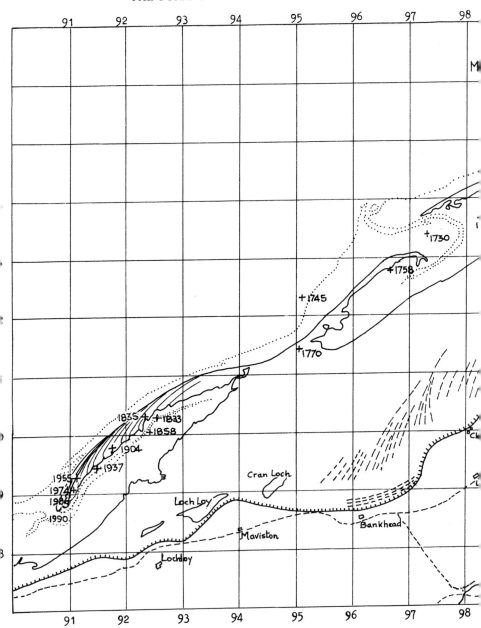

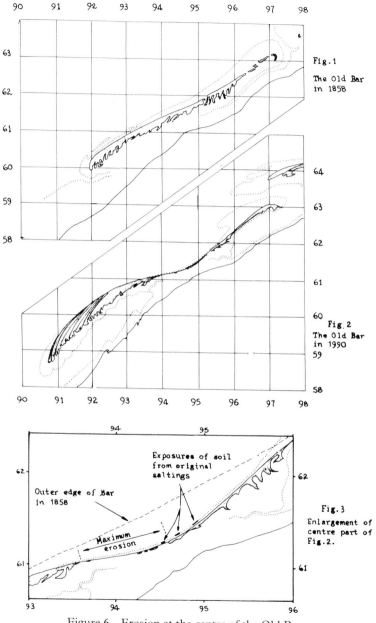

Fig.1
The Old Bar
in 1858

Fig.2
The Old Bar
in 1990

Exposures of soil
from original
saltings

Outer edge of Bar
in 1858

Maximum
erosion

Fig.3
Enlargement of
centre part of
Fig.2.

Figure 6    Erosion at the centre of the Old Bar.

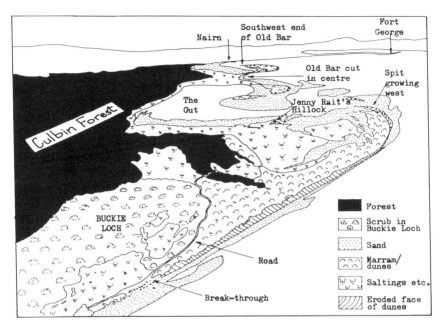

Figure 7    The Buckie Loch and the Old Bar in 1984.

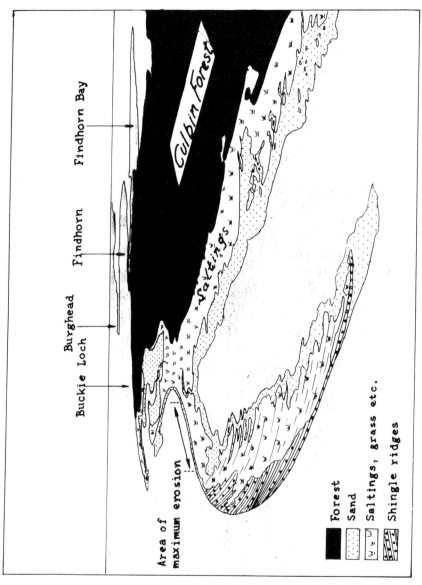

Figure 8   The Old Bar in 1979, looking north east.

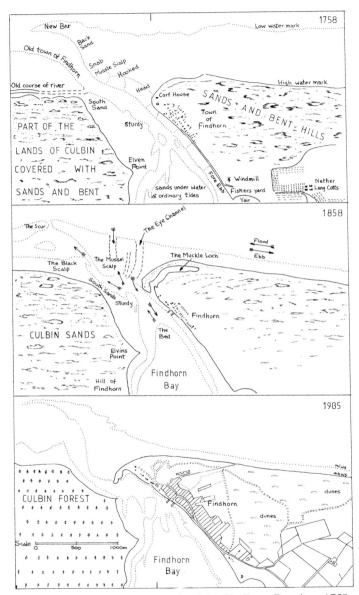

Figure 9    The westward growth of the Findhorn Bar since 1758.

Plate 4   Old ploughed rigs in the Culbin Sands, c.1938.

Figure 10    Part of Brodie Estate in 1770, from map by George Brown.

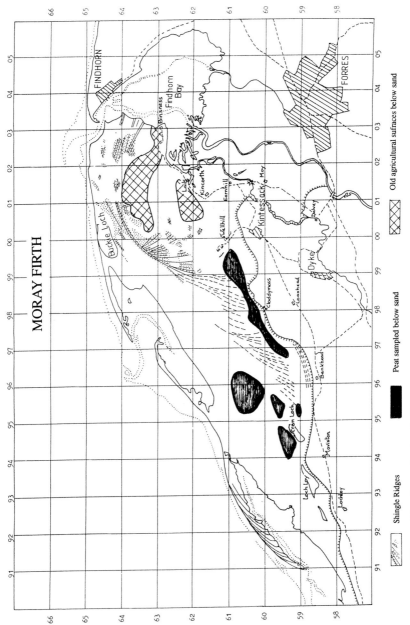

Figure 11   Areas in the Culbin Forest where peat and soils have been sampled below the sand.

Old agricultural sufraces below sand

Peat sampled below sand

Shingle Ridges

MORAY FIRTH

FINDHORN

FORRES

Findhorn Bay

Buckie Loch

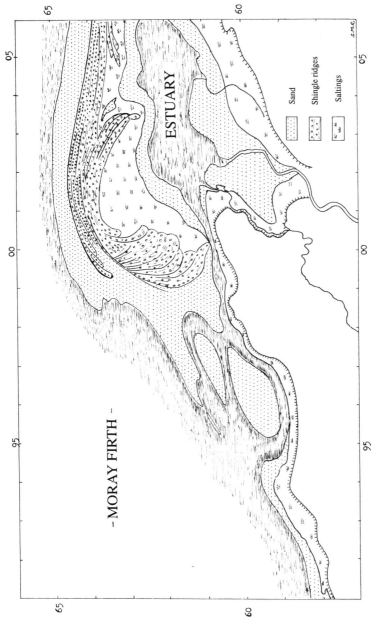

Sand

Shingle ridges

Saltings

ESTUARY

- MORAY FIRTH -

Figure 12    The development of saltings with falling sea level.

# SEA LEVEL CHANGE AND THE ORIGINS OF THE MATERIALS

## INTERPRETATION OF "RAISED BEACH" DEPOSITS

Early researchers into the problems of sea level changes felt compelled to make their findings conform to the dogma of the "25, 50 and 100-foot beaches," which had been accepted as the levels for the late and post glacial seas. More recently there followed a period during which it was fashionable to force evidence from surveys made at widely separated points across the country into a unified theory of isostatic recovery for the whole of the UK. This approach was regarded by Flemming (1982) as being statistically unrealistic, taking into consideration the smallness of the sample and the wide geographical scatter of the points. However there are now signs of a wind change starting to blow, with geographers embarking on a widespread reappraisal of the whole problem of sea level changes and the forces governing them, in light of the evidence from offshore surveys and modern theories of earth crustal movements.

The extensive superficial deposits blanketing the coastal lowlands of the Inner Moray Firth show features which, over the years, have been variously interpreted as providing proof that after the decline of the Scottish Ice Sheet, sea level rose to heights of up to 46m above that of the present day.

Peacock (1968) considered that scattered small areas of gravel at varying heights between 27m and 15m at Lossiemouth, and along the Covesea-Roseisle ridge were associated with higher shorelines—figures which were in close agreement with Ogilvie (1923). He also traced a beach margin from near Forres eastwards to Coltfield, which sloped gently from west to east, and he suggested this was a late-glacial beach which had later been tilted by differential isostatic recovery in the manner proposed by Sissons (1963), adding that other examples might well have been masked by variable factors. In his examination of deposits near Inverness, Peacock (1977) related the formations to a sea level of 30m above the present, while Synge (1977), looking at the same area and also at Ardersier and Nairn, concluded that the sea had reached a maximum level of 46m. A clay deposit at about 25m O.D. at Allanfearn, between Inverness and Ardersier, Synge considered could have been a marine deposit laid down when the ice margins stood at Inverness. Sissons (1981) considered that sea level at

Inverness had reached 28m. All these raised beach features above 10m O.D. are established in superficial materials deposited during the deglaciation of the area.

Synge (1956) had envisaged an ice sheet with one limb over the Moray Firth and another over the Central Highlands: linked in the west but leaving a "Moraineless Buchan" in the east. Peacock (1968) presented evidence for, at one stage, the ice to have covered the Laich of Moray, while the open sea reached in to the mouth of the River Spey. Later, (1971), he investigated the "Coastal Deposits" of Banffshire, first described by Read (1923), and concluded that they were fresh-water sands and gravels laid down in temporary lakes and channels ponded against the edge of an ice-sheet covering the Moray Firth. These deposits extended from near Cullen to Banff, with the drainage then continuing SE through the channel now occupied by the Deveron and into the Ythan Basin. He could not find a satisfactory link between this sequence and his earlier interpretation of events farther west.

Chesher and Lawson (1983) show, on a bathymetric chart of the Moray Firth, a deep offshore trough lying from the Inner Moray Firth to about 8km north of Lossiemouth, and from there turning gradually east to run roughly parallel to the coast to beyond Fraserburgh. The trough is 70m below sea level off Lossiemouth and deepens to 200m towards Fraserburgh. This trough was eroded where the Moray ice was at its thickest and where the base had reached it's pressure melting point. In contrast, the ice lying to the south was thinner and remained frozen to the land surface causing no erosion. This interpretation gives a more satisfactory explanation of Synge's "Moraineless Buchan" for an area that lay well to the cold continental side of the maximum snowfall line. It also explains the survival of tors in the Cairngorms and the deeply weathered gabbros in Aberdeenshire: both stemming from sub-tropical weathering.

Chesher and Lawson also describe rhythmically laminated silt and mud deposits found in a borehole 14.8m below the seabed in 156m of water in the basin north of Banff. These were laid down in the quiet waters of a lake occupying part of the basin at the time of the retreat of the Moray Firth Ice. Carbon 14 analysis of wood fragments within the laminated sequence gave dates averaging 14,000 BP, indicating that at that time the open sea still lay some distance to the northeast. It does not, however, give any indication as to the position of the ice at that time.

Their mapping of the sea bed deposits shows a broad stream of gravel 5.0 to 10.0km wide, extending along the coast from the mouth of the Spey for 70km eastwards towards Fraserburgh. This can be interpreted as being an ice-edge-controlled meltwater spread. Off the mouth of the Spey the gravels are very coarse, becoming finer and more sandy eastwards. The deposits may be the result of the catastrophic sub-glacial drainage of ice-dammed lakes farther up the Spey valley, dating from a later stage than the Banff Coastal Deposits.

Recognition of the importance of fluvio-glacial processes has only in recent years been gaining ground, as researchers study present day glaciers and apply their findings to the evidence nearer home: e.g. Boulton, (1972): Sugden and John, (1976). This has led to a better appreciation of the vast amounts of debris transported and dumped by the torrential meltwater streams. From the orientation and distribution of meltwater channels and fluvio-glacial deposits over Lower Moray there is strong evidence that, in the retreat stage of the last Scottish ice sheet, meltwaters issuing from the Great Glen, Strath Nairn and the Findhorn valley were being channeled ENE along, and at times ponded against, the margin of an ice sheet covering what is today the Moray Firth and adjacent coasts.

With this in mind, the features taken by early workers as evidence of high sea levels can be seen to be the products of ice-marginal drainage channels or lakes. Synge's 46m beach was a marginal drainage channel at the exit to the Great Glen and his "marine" clay at lower level, which was non-fossiliferous, could equally well have formed in an ice margin lake. Peacock's sloping beach fits perfectly into a series of marginal terraces that can be traced at levels below 21m on the east side of Forres. The patchy gravels at higher levels at Lossiemouth and on the Covesea-Roseisle ridge can equally well be interpreted as ice marginal deposits from the time these rocky knolls stood up above the ice, and it will later be shown that the shingle making up these high level "beach deposits" differs from the true beach shingles at lower levels.

Today, along the exposed stretch of Spey Bay, waves form storm beach shingle ridges reaching some 5.5m above the sand and mark the head of the beach. It would be a reasonable assumption that the head of any former beach might be marked by a ridge of similar dimensions. Just inland from the coast at Spey Bay, Lossiemouth, Burghead Bay and in the Culbin Forest are extensive stretches of shingle ridges reaching up to some 11m above present sea level, indicating that the sea has stood at a level of approximately 5.5m O.D. before falling back to leave this evidence behind. The ridges show text book depositional features, identical to those of the modern beaches, while none of these can be found in the higher level "beach deposits". At this same level of 5.5m O.D. there is a wave-cut platform, cut into solid rock along the Moray Coast. Because of the short period the sea stood at this level, this is considered to be a re-occupied feature, dating from a much earlier period.

It now seems logical to think of the Late Glacial Period as being a time when the huge ice sheets locked up so much water (in the form of ice) that sea level stood some 80m lower than that of the present day. Instead of a theory according to which the land emerged from a "100 foot sea" it is now considered that, as the ice melted, there was a gradual rise of sea level from this low level to one a little below that of today where it stabilised for a short time. Around 6500 BP a further rise to 5.5m above present sea level occurred. This is known as the Post Glacial High Sea Level, after which the sea fell back to today's level.

## THE ORIGINS OF THE MATERIALS

The Culbin Foreland has an area of some 28 square kilometres, a large part of which is covered by spectacular sand dunes, while the northeastern half also has impressive spreads of storm beach shingle ridges formed when sea level stood higher than it does today. The shingle ridges are at their highest in the east, where they reach 9.0m O.D., while the dunes are of all sizes up to 30m in height. This vast array of dunes and ridges have for long fascinated both expert and layman, and while there are no shortages of theories as to the sources of the materials which go to build up the Culbin, there has been very little detailed work done on the problem.

Most authors were happy to state that the Rivers Findhorn and Nairn brought down large amounts of sand and gravel to the sea. This was then moved west along the coast under the action of the tides, and after being thrown up on the beaches, was blown back northeastwards as the ever-moving Culbin sand-hills. Just to be sure, supplementary sources were added: erosion of the beaches in the innermost part of the Firth to the west, erosion of the beaches in Burghead Bay, erosion of the sandstone cliffs of the Black Isle, erosion of the Old Red Sandstone rocks on the sea bed, widespread inundation by exceptional storms, uplift of the sea bed, sand blow from the 100 foot beach, etc.

## THE VARIOUS THEORIES OF THE ORIGIN OF THE SAND IN THE CULBIN

1791    DUNBAR in *Old Statistical Account*: The converging coastline of the Inner Moray Firth increases the effects of inundations from storms coming from the open northeast.

1798    GRANT & LESLIE: Some dreadful commotions both of land and water amassed the ample store for such ruinous accumulations. The sand may have come from losses near the head of the Firth.

1837    MARTIN: At a former period it would appear some terrible hurricanes and convulsions had taken place, not only on the coast of Moray, but etc. Both shingle and sand thrown up. Sand proceeded from Maviston Hills.

1839 RHIND: Shores of Moray Firth have been considerably raised above their former level. We have thus a large tract of arenaceous accumulations raised up out of the ocean and exposd in such a way to be easily drifted by the prevailing winds of the district.

1842 DUFF: The magazine of sand which supplied the materials of the innundation had been raised from the bed of the ocean at the same time as the beaches of rolled boulders, and being acted on by the wind, which prevails from the southwest, had been wafted in a fearfully devastating course, and deposited over the rich and fertile fields of Culbin, as well as a rich tract of country lying to the eastward of the river Findhorn.

1854 MILLER: ... and the winds blew and the ocean beds were upheaved to the air and the light, and the waves threw upon the shore, from arenaceous sea-bottoms, their accumulations of light sand.

1859 MILLER: The land rose, apparenty during severe interupted paroxysms of upheaval, so that there was a fringe of comparatively level sea bottom laid dry, and added to the country's area, considerably broader than that at which we now see exposed by the ebb of every stream tide.

1880 CRAIG: Culbin had deep alluvial soil formed of the fine silt brought down by the Findhorn at a remote period. The sand came partly from the denudation of the cliff bounding the Culbin to the south, which is of stratified sand. Quotes HORNE who wrote that part of the sediment was carried down by the Findhorn and part was the sand blown from these 100 foot beach sand deposits.

1888 CRAIG: Mentions the drift on the 100 foot terrace and that the Findhorn carries an enormous quantity of sand at present to the sea every year.

1893 MURDOCH: Culbin contains 50 million tons of sand. The Findhorn discharges sand into the bay and this is circulated to the west by tides and then blown back by the wind.

1896 WALLACE: The sand came chiefly from the sea, being carried down partly by the rivers and partly by erosion of the Old Red Sandstone of the sea floor. These were added to the drift from the 100 foot terrace.

1897 MACKIE: from his study of sand grains deduced that they originated from the sands of the rivers Nairn and Findhorn (in large part) and named Ardclach and Kinsteary granites as the source. No theory of deposition given.

1923 HORNE: Re-states his study quoted by Wallace (1896). Sand came to sea via the River Findhorn ever since glacial times: it travels west in the tide and blows back in the wind. Wind-blown sand from the "various beaches" is probably added to this.

1923    OGILVIE: The sand circulation in through the dunes and back to the southwest along the shore, etc.

1937    STEERS: The sand comes from the River Findhorn and from erosion of the coast farther east.

1950    OVINGTON: Sand from the rivers suplemented by sand from older raised beaches.

1966    JOHNSTONE: Sand has come to the sea via the Findhorn since glacial times: travels west in sea currents and is blown back northeastwards by winds.

1976    EDLIN: The rivers Findhorn and Nairn, when in spate, carry a substantial burden of sand and gravel, mostly derived from the erosion of glacial deposits in the upper reaches. Erosion of soft sandstone cliffs also contributes (of this he says "illustrated by the cliffs of the Black Isle across the Firth").

1978    RITCHIE: et al. ... of this extensive foreland is a result of the redistribution and reworking of vast amounts of fluvioglacial sands and gravels associated with deglaciation followed by a steady falling sea level. In post-glacial times the River Findhorn flowed into a wide open bay, and deposited large volumes of sand and shingle, which were subsequently covered with blown sand.

1981    GAULD: Follows the 27m Ogilvie beach story, with falling sea level. Sand filled up the bay leading to the development of dunes.

The study of the sand grains from the Culbin dunes by Mackie (1897) was the first scientific investigation into the problem. Here Mackie recognised that the quartz and feldspar grains were similar to those found in the rivers Findhorn and Nairn, though they were more rounded by wind action and, due to the distances travelled, contained a smaller proportion of the more fragile feldspars. He considered that these grains had originated from the Ardclach and Kinsteary (Park) granites, and that a large part of the sand in Culbin had come from these rivers.

Detailed mapping of the area was done by Oglivie (1923) prior to afforestation. He considered that the sand circulated in the tide and wind, but applying the new theories of longshore drift, he was of the opinion that the shingle bars of Culbin were at one stage continuous with those inland of Burghead Bay. Steers (1937), in a more detailed study of both parts, thought there was no connection between the shingle ridges on either side of Findhorn Bay. He agreed with Oglivie as to the circulation of the sand, adding that, while some sand came from the river, some came from the erosion of the coast farther to the east.

From that date, the matter was more or less settled. Ogilvie and Steers were quoted for mapping and development by all later writers, and Mackie's sand-grain study confirmed the rivers as the source of the sand.

Ross (1976) and Ritchie et al. (1978) considered the materials to be fluvioglacial in origin. Most tied in their theories with emergence from a sea level of 25 to 30m above that of the present day.

Findhorn Bay acts as a giant settling tank for the deposition of suspended solids brought down by the river. Closer examination shows that the river gravel is dumped as soon as the channel widens out where the flow reaches the southern side of the bay, and that over the whole of the bay the surface is of silt grade or in places silty sand. Although in severe spates the gravel may be carried farther, it does not transgress very far into the bay. It is of interest here to note that after the 1829 spate, the bay was found to have shallowed by 45cm (Aitken 1842). The raised storm beach shingle ridges (fig. 5) form the backbone of the Culbin Foreland, and while some of the sand in the Culbin may have been brought down by the river, the shingle certainly did not pass through the bay or any earlier lagoon.

In the course of an unrelated investigation by the present writer into the source of volcanic rocks found in the shingle of the beaches of Moray, some interesting facts emerged which threw light on the processes involved in the building of the Culbin Foreland.

It had been noted that there were significant numbers of pebbles of brecciated andesite, hornblende andesite and rhyolite in the shingle on the beach at Burghead Bay. Lavas of these types do not appear on geological maps of the area. Wallace (1880) mentioned conglomerates of Old Red Sandstone age occurring near Buckie as containing abundant volcanic materials, but repeated attempts to trace this rock failed. Similarly no pebbles of volcanic origin were found in the conglomerates in the cliffs of the Spey and Fochabers (cf. Peacock 1968 p.33) nor in the cliffs of the Findhorn below Sluie. A few tiny pebbles of altered dacite in deeply weathered sandstone near Burgie (NJ 095 604) were the only volcanic materials found. The small outcrops of andesitic rock exposed in the Gollachy Burn and the Burn of Rannas are trachyandesites and cannot be confused with the types found on the beaches.

Systematic sampling of the beaches from the Spey to Culbin was then undertaken, and pebble counts done over areas of 2 square metres at various sites. In order to become familiar with the different rock types, thin sections were made from selected pebbles—some 60 being made by the end of the exercise. Two of the sections proved to be of withamite-bearing andesites—a rare rock type whose only known exposure in the UK is in Glencoe. The volcanic pebbles on the Moray beaches had an Old Red Sandstone "aspect", and hornblende andesites and rhyolites are also common in Glencoe and the Ben Nevis area. This immediately focused attention on that part of the world and various authorities on glaciation were consulted to see if they thought ice-transport might be the solution. They were of the opinion that, with the Moor of Rannoch being the ice-centre, a radial distribution from there could have brought the material to the Moray Coast via the Great Glen or the valleys of the Findhorn or Spey.

Pebble counts (Appendix 4) and sampling were then continued westwards to try to prove the Great Glen had been the supply route. A significant difference in beach materials was found at Nairn, 3km southwest of the Culbin Bar, where only isolated pebbles of the volcanic materials occurred. By Ardersier, 12km southwest of the bar, these too were absent. A further 8km to the southwest a few pebbles of brecciated andesite were found on the north side of Alturlie Point while none were present on the beach at the west side. No volcanic materials were found in the gravel pits in the huge fluvioglacial deposits at the point and none were found in the even larger gravel workings at Torvaine in the mouth of the Great Glen at Inverness. This effectively ruled out the suggestion of the materials having travelled north via the Great Glen.

A wider sampling exercise was then undertaken, in course of which every visible gravel pit, fluvioglacial terrace, spread of river gravel, roadside cutting etc., between Glencoe and the Moray Firth as far as the Aberdeenshire boundary were visited—a total of 296 sites in all, in a project which took several years to complete. This indicated that the volcanic pebbles were concentrated along the coast from the Old Bar of Culbin in the west, eastwards to Banffshire. They also occurred in the inland shingle ridges of Culbin, Burghead Bay and Spey Bay. Away from the coast they were not found, but they did occur in the River Spey upstream as far as Carron Bridge (NJ 224 411). Irregularly rounded boulders of brecciated andesite up to 30cm across were found in the Spey near Craigellachie Bridge (NJ 286 454) and as these were the largest found in the survey, it was hoped that the source might be somewhere in that vicinity, but no volcanic rock was found in situ.

From the study of coastal processes at work along the Moray Coast at the present time, and also from local records and maps going back some 300 years, it can be said with confidence that the unconsolidated materials on the beaches behave exactly as described in modern text books on the subject. The largest waves come in from the open northeast sector and the materials are moved westwards along the coast in the longshore drift, with shingle bars and hooked spits building across the river mouths. Today we see the bar building west across the mouth of the Spey at up to 40m per year, necessitating a cut having to be made through the shingle every 15 years or so to protect the village of Kingston from the encroaching river channel (Plate 1). Over the past 232 years the Old Bar at Culbin has averaged a 14.5m per year westward movement and the new bar at the mouth of Findhorn Bay, where there is now a much reduced supply of shingle, has extended at 2.3m per year over the same period.

This theory can also be applied to the original developments along the Moray Coast after the retreat of the Moray Firth Ice Sheet. As the ice withdrew, vast spreads of gravel were being deposited eastwards along it's margin by meltwaters issuing from the Spey valley. These have been mapped by Chesher and Lawson (1983) as forming a belt up to 10km wide stretching eastwards for 70km from the mouth of the Spey. After the ice had dispersed, these gravels were reworked by the rising sea to form storm beach ridges and offshore bars. By the peak of the Post Glacial High Sea Level of 5.5m, which occured around 6500 BP, these ridges and bars had migrated landwards to the positions shown in fig. 17.6. The shingle ridges and hooked spits are phenomena of the high tide mark, and with the abundant supply of materials the growth of the westwards-building bars was rapid. As they lengthened, they were periodically breached, and the process began again, with the development of new bars at the river mouths, while the remnants of the former ones continued to drift westwards to supply material for the formation of later features there. When sea level began to fall, the higher ridges were left high and dry, safe from erosion, and a fresh series formed at progressively lower levels on their seaward side.

Such a linked bar and shingle ridge sequence, drawing its materials from the Spey gravels and extending as far west as the Culbin is necessary to explain:

(i) The presence of hard Moinian and igneous rocks forming the shingle along beaches where the only *in situ* rocks are sandstones.

(ii) How the beach gravels crossed river mouths and estuaries.

(iii) The formation and details of the inland fossil bars and ridges that we see today, and the sequence of their development.

The development of the Culbin foreland is dealt with in detail in the following chapter.

A growing number of reseachers are now of the opinion that most of the material on modern beaches was not carried to the sea by present day rivers but dates from the glacial era when erosion was at its height and meltwater torrents were transporting huge volumes of debris. This does not invalidate Mackie's (1897) theory that much of the sand in Culbin originated from the Ardclach and Kinsteary granites and was transported to the sea by the rivers. The expression "hard as granite" is purely relative. Boulders of granite disintegrate surprisingly quickly when being pounded over a gravel river bed during a spate or by wave action on shingle beaches. This is borne out by the small numbers of granite pebbles found in the survey. An ice-margin controlled meltwater drainage system over lower Nairn and Moray would have carried granitic debris from the Ardclach and Kinsteary areas east-northeastwards, but eventually it would almost all have finished up in marginal lakes and channels. The rise of the Post Glacial Sea meant that large masses of sand in the form of beach deposits were moved landwards with the migrating shore zone, and these included the reworked materials from the old meltwater deposits.

# THE DEVELOPMENT SEQUENCE

With the likely origin of the materials forming the backbone of the Culbin Foreland being the Spey Gravels, and assuming the coastal processes involved were of a similar nature to those of the present day, a detailed sucession of events can only be worked out if the whole coastal section from the Old Bar of Culbin in the west to the River Spey in the east, is treated as a single unit. Any development sequence must not be out of line with the field evidence offered by the many exposures along this stretch which are listed in Appendix 5.

## DEVELOPMENTS BETWEEN THE SPEY AND ROSEISLE

By the completion of the deglaciation of northeast Scotland, sea level had begun to rise, but was still far below that of the present day. The "dry" surface of the Moray Firth was covered by extensive spreads of glacial debris, and there was a huge fan of gravel extending north and east from the mouth of the Spey.

Waves from the rising Post Glacial Sea began to rework these deposits and storm beach shingle ridges formed along the high water mark, moving landwards as sea level rose. The eastward-flowing waters of the Spey were diverted westwards as the ridges, driven by the longshore drift, spread in stages towards the Inner Moray Firth. By 6500 BP the sea had reached its highest level, 5.5m above that of the present day, and the channel of the Spey ran westwards along the north face of the Bin Hill of Garmouth. (The hill is not "carved from Old Red Sandstone" as suggested by Ogilvie (1923) and Steers (1937), but is a huge mound of fluvio-glacial sands and gravel (Aitken et al 1979). Erosion processes then, were exactly as we see now along this stretch, with bars continuing to grow west across the river mouth, and periodically being breached by the river when in spate. The remnants of earlier bars were spread westwards along the coast (fig. 17).

As the sea fell back to its present day level, a succession of shingle ridges 800m in width was left high and dry between the Bin Hill and the sea, and extending westwards to Lossiemouth (Plate 1). These give some measure of the supply of the shingle available at the start of the process.

The ridges were mapped by Oglivie (1923) and Peacock (1968) who gave differing interpretations as to the stages in the westward progress of the shingle, but agreed on the main point that a stage was reached when the ridges built west to link on to the "island" of Branderburgh. The short, recurved bars southwest of Lossiemouth point to this not having been a single stage, but at least two.

Once this eastern exit was firmly closed, the waters of the Lossie were diverted westwards from the lagoon filling the Spynie Depression and on towards Roseisle, where they flowed into the estuary which was developing in the shelter of the bar system growing west from Burghead. Materials forming this bar had passed west along the north side of the Covesea—Roseisle ridge. This drainage pattern continued until the eastern bar was breached. The remnants of this breach are seen today as the splendid set of recurved shingle ridges near Caysbrigggs (NJ 250 674), but which are now being obscured by gravel workings.

Looking at the possible link from Loch Spynie to Roseisle in more detail, a simplified map of the superficial deposits and rock outcrops of Lower Moray (fig. 17.1) shows a long, low-lying depression, filled with estuarine deposits, flanked on the landward side by fluvioglacial sands and gravels, and on the seaward side by a series of fossil raised beach shingle deposits and the sandstone ridge lying between Lossiemouth and Burghead Bay.

Early attempts to use the contours on Ordnance Survey maps of Lower Moray as a guide to low level features had been abandoned as the lines were unbelievably inaccurate in editions prior to 1979. In addition in the Culbin Sands area, coastal and bar details had not been updated since the turn of the century, in spite of major changes. This led to unexpected practice in elementary surveying. (Complaint was met with the quick response that the Admiralty were responsible for the mapping of the coast at that time).

The general form of a map of Lower Moray "submerged" to the 8m contour (fig. 17.2) presents a strong suggestion that at one time a drainage channel linked the Spynie Depression with Roseisle and Kinloss. Tracing any such channels has been made difficult by many processes which have smoothed out the landscape over the 5000 years which have intervened since they developed; the establishment of vegetation and soils, the change in drainage patterns, the growth of peat in abandoned channels and downhill soil creep have all contributed. In historical times there are records of sand-blowing, peat-stripping and drainage, followed by the development of modern agricultural land patterns.

The landsurface of the area was considerably altered by lengthy periods of sand-blowing in the late 17th and early 18th centuries and records include the mention of agricultural lands near Roseisle being covered by 1 to 2m of sand: Peacock (1968) describes banks of peat now below 1.2m of sand in the same area. Present day deep-drainage schemes have lowered the water table and permitted fuller use of the land for agriculture, further obscuring old features. Fortunately some old estate plans from the area still survive. A map of Spynie Loch dated 1783 (in Mackintosh 1928 and fig. 13) showed the Loch extending 7.5km from Kintrae in the west to the Lossie at Caysbriggs in the east. A plan by Wm. Anderson, dated 1749 and headed "A Plan of His Grace the Duke of Gordon and Sir Robert Gordon's Estate and Mosses in the West End of the Parish of Duffus" (Scottish Record Office RHP 2016) showed in great detail the position of former peat mosses and shallow lochs in the area (fig. 14). Another plan of the same area by Alex. Taylor dated 1773 (RHP 2004) is not so accurate across the sheet, but in using the two together, a wealth of detail can be gleaned.

The positions of some of these small lochs had been lost in time, and though referred to in old writings, surviving small-scale maps of the period gave conflicting evidence as to their existence. Of particular interest is the position of Outlet Loch with the mill and milldam which stood on the stream flowing from the loch into Burghead Bay. The loch is shown as being over 1km long and 300m at its widest point, in a position which today lies in the Roseisle Forest, west to east across the B 9089 road, 500m northeast of Wards. Here the Forestry Commission has recently (1986) felled a large part of the forest, and there is now, for the first time, a clear view of the flat nature of the ground on the east side of the road where part of the loch lay. The area had been deep-drained and trees planted on a deposit of blown sand covering the old loch site. The Outlet was described by Macfarlane (1723) as supporting a large population of wildfowl. Leslie (1811) reported one mill demolished and the other little used because of the blowing sand, but that the waters from the Loch of Inchstellie still flowed sluggishly into the bay, and with a little effort the mill could be brought back into use. Young (1871) refers to blown sand having filled the Lochs of Roseisle, Outlet and Keam, and the burns which originally drained them diverted to flow into the Loch of Spynie. During the late 18th century parts of the Black Moss south of Buthill were still under water and a boatman ferried people across it (Wallace 1896 p.114). The peat mosses of Lower Hempriggs and Hatton survied until more recent times and probably occupied old drainage channels leading to Findhorn Bay. In 1849 parts of the horns of a large Bos primigenius (giant ox) were found in drainage cuttings at Westfield (Gordon 1859).

From his investigations into the form of the Spynie Depression, Peacock (1968) found that over 30m of glacial and marine sediments filled the basin. He considered that a major fault ran west to east from Burghead Bay through the Spynie Depression and was marked by a rock-cut channel.

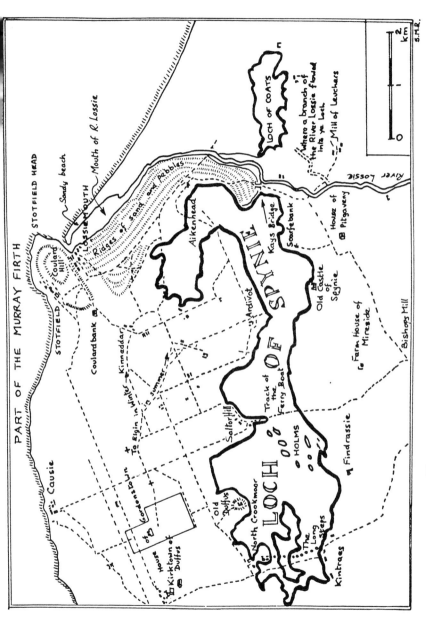

Figure 13 The Loch of Spynie in 1783 by Hugh Kinnaird.

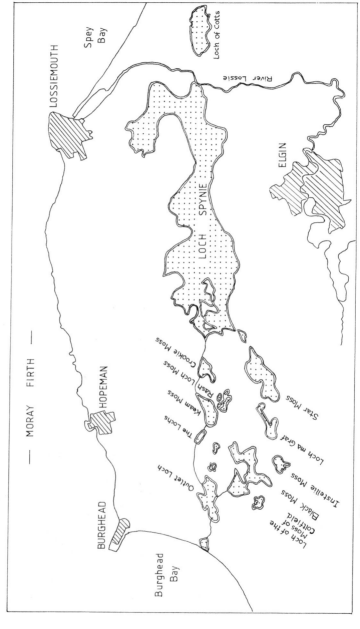

Figure 14   The lochs and mosses between Spey Bay and Burghead Bay in 1749.

Geophysical and borehole evidence suggested the deepest part of the trough was 37m below O.D. and some 425m wide. A borehole at East Mains (NJ 2044 6672) showed rockhead to be 30.8m below O.D. with a cover of 11.8m of glacial deposits, 12.6m of estuarine clays and 6.4m of marine sediments on top. Similar thicknesses of clay were known from old clay pits in the area.

At Roseisle Maltings (NJ 124 655) under layers of sand and silty clays reaching down to at least 3.0m below OD, bedrock occurs at 10m below OD. Part of this site lies with the western boundary of the Black Moss shown in fig. 14, and the top layer of sand is probably the same cover of blown sand seen in the old site of the Outlet Loch a few hundred metres to the northeast.

Weakened rocks along the fault line would have been scoured out by ice action to form a deep trough, and with the rockhead lying well below present sea level probably acted as a drainage channel over a considerable period. The existance of such a channel was proposed by Ogilvie (1923) and Peacock (1968) and has to be fitted into a sequence of events that agrees with the evidence exposed at Burghead Bay.

## THE SUBMERGED FOREST IN BURGHEAD BAY

The descriptions given by various writers over the past two centuries of the presence of a submerged forest in Burghead Bay have been widely used as evidence for sea level having stood at a lower level than that of the present day. The forest was described as being embedded in a layer of peat, and a problem arises when one compares what can be seen of the peat today with the accounts of the old observers.

Stretches of peat and peaty soil occur near low water mark towards the east side of Burghead Bay and are occasionally exposed during periods when the sand level on the beach is low. The beds extend discontinuously over a distance of 3km, and at their thickest measure 27cm, overlying stretches of coarse rounded cobbles and boulders, many of which are of local Permo-Triassic sandstone and chert. At one stage in 1983, one band of peaty soil 350m wide was exposed from low water mark to within 70m of the top of the beach. In the more southwesterly of the exposures the peat contained flattened reed material, but quickly graded northeastwards into sandy estuarine soil. It was noted that over the short period during which this soil had no covering of sand, it quickly crumbled away under wave action, and large areas were completely stripped. No tree stumps, logs or twigs have been seen in these beds of peat, and any fragments dislodged by wave action appear to have been pounded to pieces rather than rafted up the beach. A similar thin peaty soil was found in boreholes on the airfield at 1.7m below OD (NJ 072 638).

A complex of storm beach shingle ridges which formed when sea level stood some 5.5m higher than today, lies just inland along the margins of Burghead Bay (fig. 15). Today the waves are actively attacking the seaward side of this stretch, cutting a fresh "cliff face" in the unconsolidated sands and shingle along the entire 10km length of the bay. The result is a sedimentologist's dream—an uninterrupted vertical section many km in length, cut down through the old beach sediments up to 7.5m thick, which were deposited on top of marine clays and silts and stretches of peaty soils below present sea level (Plate 5). Low stretches of the "cliff" have a capping of later estuarine soils and modern blown sand. Sections in the centre and east of Burghead Bay, where the "cliff" is up to 5.5m high, occasionally reveal a shingle land surface, heavily soil-stained. Here later fresh water drainage channels cut down through the marine deposits in

Plate 5    Sand and shingle layers of raised beach deposits forming "cliffs" in Burghead Bay.

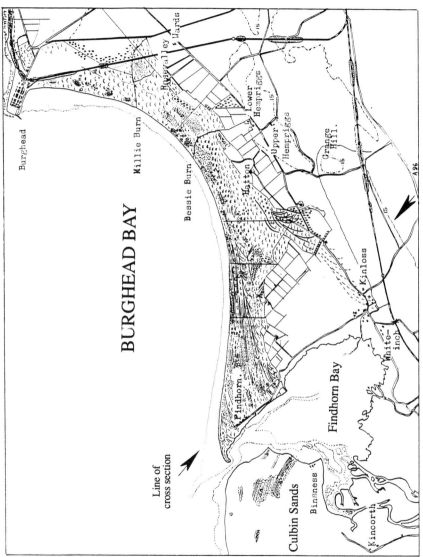

Figure 15   The shingle ridges flanking Burghead Bay: modified from Balchin (in Steers, 1937).

the "cliff", and are now filled with peat and blown sand. These channels are the remains of the drainage westwards from the estuary of the Lossie, when that river's direct passage to the sea was blocked by a shingle bar. Once the Lossie breached the bar the old channels were abandoned and became shallow lochs and peat bogs as shown in fig. 14.

The peat is up to 75cm thick and underlain by a layer of pale green, unfossiliferous silt just above high water mark, and overlain by blown sand deposits which are in sharp contrast to the pebbly marine strata. Just west of the Bessie Burn (NJ 096 563), where over 600m of peat are exposed, large tree stumps and fallen logs are seen on the top surface of the peat which is made up largely of matted reeds and twigs. These beds lie some 3 to 4m higher than those seen near the low water mark farther east (Plate 6).

The earliest reference to the peat is made by Shaw (1775). "On the confines of the parishes of Duffus and Alves there is a small bay which, about 60 years ago or a little more, was a moss, in which they digged up great roots of trees, and abundance of peats, and now a 500 ton ship may ride at anchor in it. And when, some years ago, I viewed it, I found that, if the sea shall encroach farther, and rise about four feet higher, it will overflow and drown all the plains of Duffus, Kinedar and Innes. Like the encroachment it begins to make at the town of Findhorn."

Grant and Leslie (1798) describe how, prior to 1701, "Many roots and trunks of oak and fir trees were then found on the moor, and a few are still dug up in the Moss of Hatton, confirming the truth of the tradition that a forest once occupied what is now the bottom of the sea, and the downs between Findhorn and Duffus. The sand banks oppose a feeble barrier to the power of every storm from the north, by which they are themselves forced farther on the shore, and the banks of peat earth are thereby discovered 6 or 8 feet below the sand."

Martin (1836), under the heading of "Peat, Subterranean and Submarine Forests", describes how part of a submarine forest "... extends a considerable distance under the sea, and vessels of any burden may sail for depth of water above it. After a storm, large masses of peat have been raised from their original position and drifted on shore, and trunks of trees, upwards of ten feet in length and four feet in circumference, found on the beach. A large mass of drifted peat is at present exposed on the beach, upwards of twenty feet in length and two feet in thickness; trunks of trees and large branches are embedded in it. If this portion may be taken as a specimen of the vast accumulation of vegetable remains extending over the district, it may serve the purpose to mention the variety of trees in it to convey some idea of the composition of the whole. The trees are chiefly oak, birch, alder, hazel and fir, with the leaves of these matted thickly together, enclosing portions of bark with hazel nuts."

Plate 6   A tree stump on peat layers in old drainage channel in "cliff", Burghead
Bay.

Duff (1842) in discussing Burghead Bay says: "Probably connected with these sandhills and raised beaches is a submarine forest in the bay of the sea which stretches southwest from Burghead. Trees of considerable size, of oak, fir and birch, are frequently cast ashore, imbedded in a thick layer of peat moss, which is incumbent on a blue clay. This peat moss is of a peculiar structure, unlike the part of our moors; it is mostly composed of the reeds and large leaves or fronds of aquatic plants, some of them exceeding a foot and a half in length. The extent of this remarkable deposit along the bay towards Findhorn is considerable: but how far it extends into the Frith is not to be ascertained on account of the depth of water."

Gordon (1859) states "a little to the west of Burghead there is a submarine forest, which must, from the circumstances of trees being occasionally dragged up by the anchors of ships riding in the bay, extend for a considerable distance beneath the sea. Part of it is exposed at low water. It is a combination of forest, lake and marsh peat."

Wallace (1896), most probably quoting from the above, says "Tradition had it that a forest once stood where the Bay of Burghead is now. Roots and trunks are still dug up in the Moss of Hatton ... etc." He goes on to say "According to the authority of the present inhabitants of Burghead, the sea has encroached on the land from 100 to 150 yards within the last 30 years: and a promontory of sand called 'The Point' near the Bessie Burn, which is between Burghead and Findhorn, has been entirely swept away during the memory of the present inhabitants."

Martin's description of the peat washed from the seabed exactly fits that of the layers exposed in the "cliff" southwest of the Bessie Burn. During northerly gales large stretches of the peat are undermined as waves attack the "cliff" and wash the silt out from below and the blown sand from above. Large rafts of peat then slump down on to the shingle and are transported along the beach in the longshore drift. No material from the other deposits below sea level survives on the shorelines. These are two totally different forms of peat, the lower one having been formed in an estuary before the Post Glacial High Sea Level of some 6500 BP and which was then buried by up to 8.5m of beach deposits. The second layer was later deposited in old river channels cut down through the marine strata after sea level fell again.

While it is impossible at this stage to know what lies on the seabed below low water mark, nothing has so far been discovered that cannot be explained by the slumping of the younger peat layer on to the beach.

A similar channel cut down into the "cliff" at the mouth of the Millie Burn (NJ 108 665) is also filled with blown sand but the base is obscured by slumping and no peat is seen. The Millie Burn at one time drained the Outlet Loch, and is on the line of the old drainage system shown in fig. 14, p.36).

# ESTUARINE DEPOSITS AND SHINGLE RIDGES ALONG BURGHEAD BAY

After a period of storms, when the sand level in the beach was low, a large area of horizontally laminated marine clay was exposed low on the beach, 300m east of the Mid Fishing Station at (NJ 066 646) (Ross & Macfarlane 1977 and Plate 7). The deposit which was approximately 1.5m below O.D. was up to 50cm thick and contained many small shells. While it was exposed it was being actively eroded by pebbles washing up and down on its upper surface. Below the clay was a layer of dark grey sandy silt containing splendidly preserved bivalves: this in turn lay on a bed of coarse cobbles similar to that underlying the estuarine soils farther east. The shell fauna was "post glacial" in age and with the present rate of erosion along this stretch of some 1.5m per annum, the clay had only recently emerged from under a cover of 8m of pebbly sand which had been deposited on top of it.

In a borehole at Findhorn, a thicker shelly marine clay band was found with a top at 2m below O.D., lying on top of a similar grey shelly silt and band of cobbles. In this case the clay had been covered by 12m of later deposits as the bore was sunk on one of the highest points of the shingle ridges. The depositional patterns in the "cliff" along Burghead Bay (Plate 5) indicate that once the marine clay was covered by sand, there had been a steady rise of beach level as the bar systems migrated shoreward with the rising Post Glacial Sea.

Fig. 15 is a simplified version of the detailed map by W.G.V Balchin in Steers (1937), which shows to advantage the complex of shingle ridges lying inland from Burghead Bay. These ridges were formed when the sea stood at up to 5.5m higher than at the present day, and were left high and dry when the sea level fell back.

A sequence of events has to be established which will accommodate the order of deposition of the various units exposed in the area and and explain the distribution of the old shingle ridges along Burghead Bay and in the Culbin Sands. (This is summarised in Appendix 5).

Balchin's splended map was surveyed before the airfield at Kinloss was constructed. In it he showed a main family of ridges extending westwards from near the Bessie Burn towards Findhorn, and a small group running southwest from the farm of Hatton for a short distance, but stopping at a small wood at the roadside. It is not at all clear why he did not show the ridges continuing southwest as far as Kinloss village as they present a continuous raised feature along this line. All the ridges he mapped were on waste ground and it may be that he did not venture in to examine the smoother outlines on agricultural land.

Boreholes and trenches confirm the structure (Appendix 7), with the

Plate 7    Bed of marine clay near low water mark, Burghead Bay.

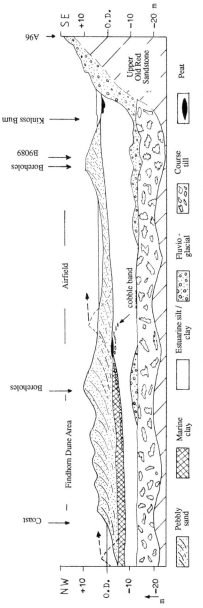

Figure 16   Simplified cross-section from Findhorn to the Kinloss Burn, along the line of section indicated in fig. 15.

shingle on the ridge coming in at 2.5m above OD, on top of the silty clay. The crest of the ridge stands at 9.0m above OD, with the ground on either side falling away to former estuarine flats. This extension of the shingle ridge system has been added to Balchin's map in fig. 15. To the north the ground rises again to 10m above OD on the main shingle ridges towards Findhorn. Evidence from boreholes, trenches and exposures along Burghead Bay suggests that a vertical sequence as shown in the cross-section of fig. 14 is necessary to explain the landward rise of the top of the silty clay and of the shingle ridges deposited on top. This suggests deposition in an estuary which was gradually narrowing by the landward migration of a series of offshore shingle bars with the rise of the Post Glacial Sea.

## THE STAGES IN THE DEVELOPMENT OF THE CULBIN FORELAND

A detailed sequence of the likely stages in this process are shown in figs. 17.1–9, and indicate the development of the Culbin Foreland.

17.1    This simplified map of superficial deposits and rock outcrops of Lower Moray is very closely related to the features in fig. 17.2.

17.2.    This shows a map of Lower Moray submerged to the 8m contour. Land below this level is mostly covered by estuarine deposits— sand, silt or clay. Features shown in black are raised storm-beach shingle ridges. Taking into account the distribution of lochs and peat mosses in fig. 14, there is a strong suggestion that connecting channels once linked the Findhorn Estuary in the west with the Spynie Basin in the east.

17.3.    By the time the Post Glacial Sea had risen to a level about 2.0m below present sea level, the shingle beach running southwest from Burghead was becoming increasingly sheltered by a large bar which was building on its seaward side. The sea remained at this level, or perhaps fell back slightly, for a long enough period for a peaty soil to develop on the thin shingle spreads which marked the open beach before the formation of the lagoon. Marine clays were deposited in the quiet waters. A similar bar system was building across the stretch from the mouth of the Spey to Lossiemouth, with the formation of a lagoon in the Spynie Basin. Here, as sea level began to rise again, marine clays and silts continued to be deposited, while in Burghead Bay the shoreward migration of the bar led to the deposition of pebbly sand on top of the marine clay and peat there. To the south side of the bar silt and clay continued to be deposited in the narrowing lagoon.

17.4. With the sea rising to about 2.0m above the present level, the plentiful materials from the Spey gravels maintained a bar-building sequence towards Lossiemouth with surplus shingle periodically passing west along the north side of the Covesea-Roseisle ridge to support further bar-building from Burghead. The original bar here had built as far as the east side of the present Culbin Sands, where it was diverting drainage from the lagoon westwards. Being temporarily starved of materials it was at this stage deeply curved and thinning at the centre in the same way as the Old Bar is at the present day (fig. 6, p.14). Small halts or oscillations in sea level meant that some beds of peat had time to form in depressions on top of the silt, before being submerged and then given a covering of thin clay.

17.5. The sea then continued to rise towards the maximum of the Post Glacial High Sea Level of 5.5m O.D. The bar advancing south over Findhorn Bay was becoming sheltered by the next development coming away from Burghead, and getting no fresh shingle, it soon breached in the centre to leave an eastern end attached to the esker of Coltfield Ridge and a severed end over the east of the Culbin. A thin cover of shingle from the breached bar was deposited on top of the clay and peat at Whiteinch (NJ 055 609) in the same way as we see today the thin shingle spreading over the saltings at the breach in the Old Bar (fig. 6). Meantime the Spynie Basin was almost completely closed off.

17.6. Still with the sea at its maximum level the eastern exit was closed, forcing the drainage from the Spynie Basin and the River Lossie to flow westwards into the Findhorn estuary through the channels and lakes which marked the remnants of the glacial trough. The new Burghead Bar, with plenty of shingle coming forward, linked on to the recurved remnant over Culbin so that the Findhorn drainage was again diverted to the west, but this time more firmly.

17.7. The increased drainage from the Spynie Basin cut more definite channels through the Burghead ridges until the eastern bar was again breached, allowing direct drainage to the sea.

17.8. At this stage sea level was falling, and as it did, fine recurves developed on the eastern bar ends with a narrow exit channel being maintained between the east and west halves. The channel from the Findhorn estuary continued to grow westward and a strongly curved hooked spit formed over Culbin, narrowing the exit channel. The first signs of emerging estuarine soils were developing.

17.9. The Findhorn broke northwards through the weak point of the retaining bar, close to the line of its present channel. With sea level falling steadily to near the present day value, a series of later shingle

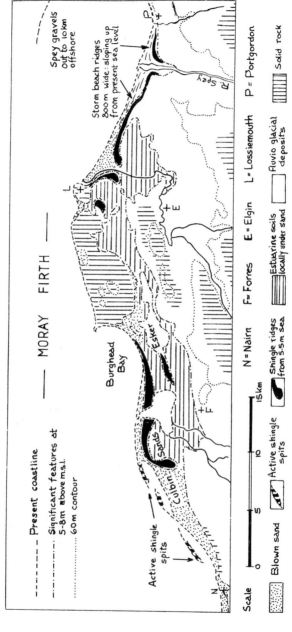

Figure 17.1   Simplified maps of the superficial deposits and rock outcrops of Lower Moray.

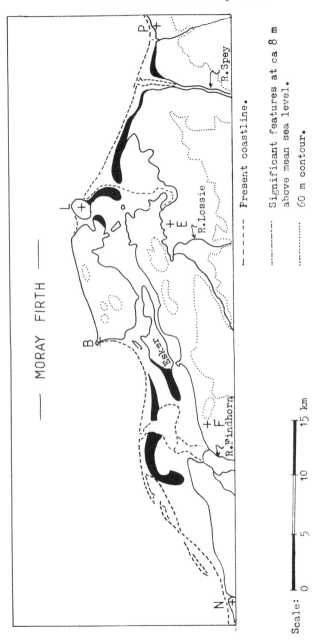

Figure 17.2   Lower Moray submerged to the 8.0m contour.

N = Nairn :  F = Forres :  B = Burghead :  L = Lossiemouth :  E = Elgin :  P = Portgordon.

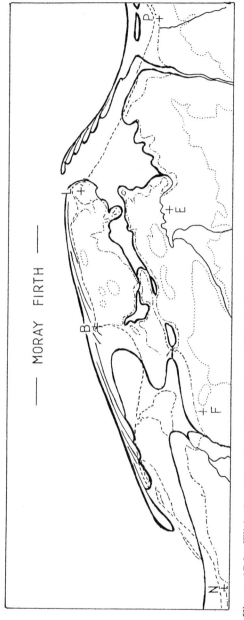

Figure 17.3   With the rising Post Glacial Sea at 2.0m below O.D., westward-growing shingle bars form sheltered estuaries.

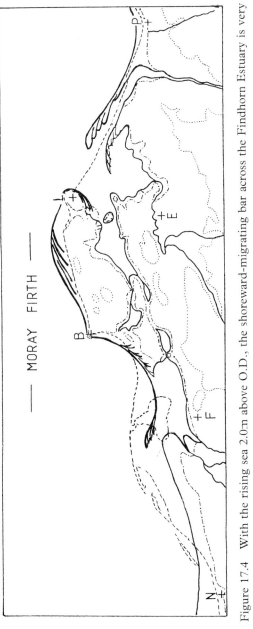

Figure 17.4   With the rising sea 2.0 m above O.D., the shoreward-migrating bar across the Findhorn Estuary is very narrow.

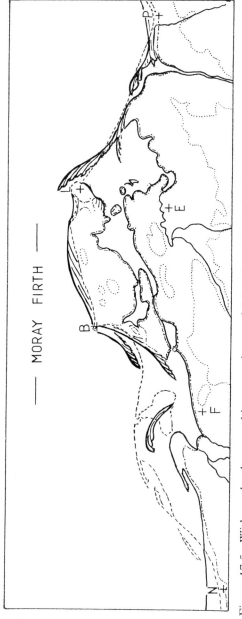

Figure 17.5  With sea level approaching a maximum of 5.5m above O.D., the bar across the Findhorn Estuary is breached, while the Spynie Basin is almost completely sealed.

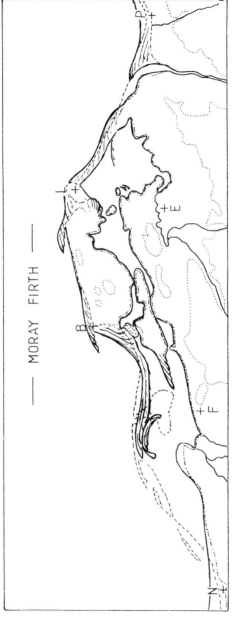

Figure 17.6   At the maximum sea level a bar builds from Burghead to link with remnants of the previous bar. The Spynie Basin is now sealed and drainage diverted westwards..

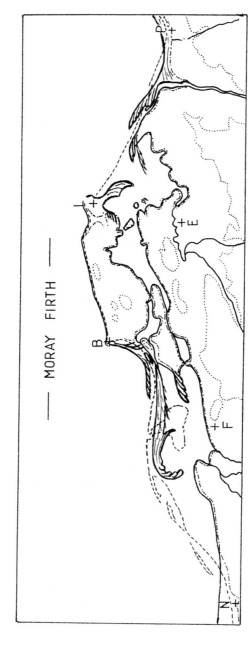

Figure 17.7  With continuing high sea level, exit channels are cut through the ridges into Burghead Bay before the Spynie Basin bar is breached.

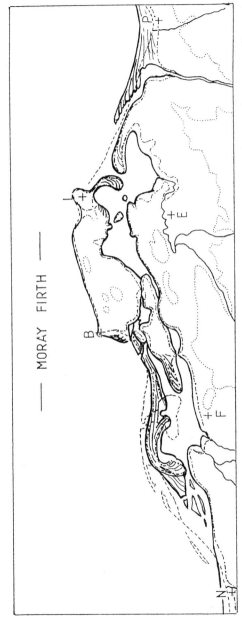

Figure 17.8  With sea level falling, the westward exit from the Findhorn Estuary lengthens and narrows. Channels into Burghead Bay are maintained, while the direct channel from the Spynie Basin remains open.

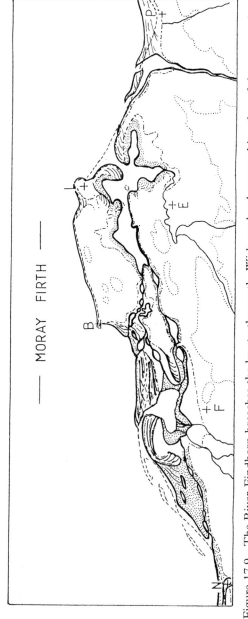

Figure 17.9    The River Findhorn breaches the bar to the north. With sea level approaching that of the present day, emerging saltings, small lochs and marshes develop.

ridges formed at progressively lower levels to the seaward of today's coastline, while streams draining into Burghead Bay continued cutting down through these beach deposits. Small lochs and peat bogs developed along the lines of abandoned channels and cross-sections through some of these are now exposed in the "cliff" along Burghead Bay. The deposits in the bay were later to be eroded back as material moved west to form the Findhorn Bar of historical times.

The sequence outlined above shows that in order to satisfy the field evidence the whole coastline from the Spey to the Culbin has to be treated as a single development unit. While future researchers will, no doubt, uncover additional features requiring some modifications to be made, the basic concept should not be greatly affected.

## THE DEVELOPMENT OF SOILS AND LAND-USE

In his study of the vegetation on the southwest end of the Old Bar, Morrison (1978) remarked on the speed at which a variety of plants had colonised the bare sand and shingle, and developed into mature cover. The northeast end of the bar, on the other hand, has suffered severe erosion, and there eroding dunes covered in marram grass top the shingle remnants. Had sea level fallen after the formation of the Old Bar, the thickening vegetation would quickly have stabilised the surface and a cap of soil would have steadily developed on top of the sand and shingle.

The extensive areas of saltings lying between the Old Bar and the Culbin Forest and the stretch between Jenny Rait's Hillock and the Buckie Loch are covered only by the highest spring tides. Here a close carpet of salt marsh grass (Puccinellia maritima) has formed and extended steadily across the flats. Other salt-resistant plants followed and the mat of vegetation thickened into a turf, developing a soil profile, and raising the general surface level. In parts, the developing soil, stabilised by the root systems of the plants, has reached 35cm in thickness.

These two units, the Old Bar and the saltings, offer us an insight into the developments on the Culbin Foreland which took place over a very much longer period of time. Once the level of the Post Glacial Sea began to fall, the first shingle ridges remained free from erosion and formed a low, dune covered promontory curving round an emerging estuary. A healthy vegetation cover developed on the dunes and over a period of several thousand years very mature soils developed. Today we see eroded remnants of these in the northeast of the Culbin Forest—the "butte-dunes", so called because these soil-capped mounds stood up above the general ground level in isolated butte- or mesa-like stretches. Gauld (1981) described them as having probably the best examples of humus podsol in Scotland, and one of the best exposures has been made a conservation area (Plate 8).

These ancient soils lie on top of well-consolidated dune sand, which in turn caps the old shingle ridges which form the backbone of the foreland. Originally this cover would have been continuous, but now, due to erosion, it is represented by isolated clusters of small mounds. The old promontory was probably covered by rank calluna and marram, but in the more easterly exposures where the soils are thicker, some horizons show layers of charcoal, indicating a scrub vegetation, periodically burned. Spreads of bare shingle partially cemented by iron-stained consolidated sand and with bands of iron pan, show where former cover has been stripped away, leaving only the leached mineral horizon as evidence of its presence. There are no indications that these soils were ever cultivated though near the inner margins, the top of the shingle is in places seen to hold a layer of dark humus.

In contrast to the raised hummock profile of the dune-covered ridges with their scrub cover, were the estuarine flats which developed in the wide lagoon into which the River Findhorn flowed (fig. 12). Like the present Findhorn Bay it was tidal and covered by fine silt and mud, which, once sea level began to fall, was rapidly colonised by salt marsh grass etc. A thickening soil developed which was later to become the farm lands of the Culbin estate. This was paralleled by similar sequences on the other side of Findhorn Bay where the low, flat-lying land, now Kinloss airfield, was to become the farm lands of Muirton.

Stretches of the old soils can still be found by digging down through the sand in hollows between the dunes (fig. 11, p.20), where a change of ground flora indicates the buried horizon. The normal forest litter gives way to a carpet of grasses and mosses, while stands of birch and willow indicate an increase in moisture content and nutrients. Old photographs taken before afforestation (Plate 4) show several old field systems with the furrows and rigs still extant. The exact locations where the photographs were taken are not known, but today one stretch of rigs can be studied in a small area some 1.1km northwest of Binsness at (NJ 0214 6354). Here the rigs are orientated north-south, and are approximately 12m wide. The soil, which can be described as a sandy loam, is now very compact, and with several dunes over 15m high in the immediate vicinity it is safe to assume that the stretch had emerged from beneath a similar depth of cover. Hugh Miller (1859) described finding "... portions of the buried furrows sorely dried into the consistence of sun-burned brick." The thickness of the soils varies from a few cm at the margins of the rigs to 30cm in the centres. The horizons lie on top of fine white sand, and the boundary

Plate 8   Ancient podsol on "butte-dune" in Culbin Forest.

between the two is usually quite sharp, forming a horizontal plane, undisturbed by ploughing.

Tregido (1982) compared soil samples from various parts of these old agricultural lands with those cultivated today on Wellhill Farm (NJ 000 611). He noted that the Wellhill soils were more sandy than those from the buried lands of Culbin, due to wind-blown sand having been mixed into them. The old soils were sufficiently compacted after burial not to have mixed with the sand. After discussing various aspects of post-burial changes, he concluded that the old Culbin soils, though light, would have been equally as fertile as those in Wellhill today. He did, however, based on observations made by Rampini (1897), assume that Culbin soils might have been fertilised by "seaware and hot dung". Seaweed might have been available along the coasts farther east but it would have been scarce or absent along the sandy shores. In any case, in the old days, with the river lying between the Culbin estate and the coast, any seaweed would have been gathered by the tenants of Muirton estate, to whom the Old Bar belonged (fig. 23, p.103). The undulating ridge of the old fossil spit formed the boundary to the arable lands of the Culbin estate and was used as grazing land. In addition it povided the tenants with marram grass for thatch and cattle bedding, grass and heather for brooms, turf for house walls and roofing and for "feal dykes". Over-exploitation of these resources and periodic burning led to severe erosion of the underlying dune sand once the turf carpet was broken. Old legends of storms being so severe that "the sand was being blown out from below the soil", have their origin here. Once a blow-out formed, the old dune sand over the shingle dried out and trickled down from underneath the soil cap, leaving it unsupported. An increase in wind removed the sand, enlarged the overhang and the slabs of soil and turf slumped on to the exposed shingle to be eroded away in turn. Even with today's cap of forest litter, the few remaining examples are slowly but surely getting smaller as the process continues.

These two distinct developments of old soils in the Culbin, differ in origin, height above sea level, age and thickness: they were put to different uses, and while the older uncultivated horizons on the shingle ridges were almost completely stripped away by wind action, the lower, flat-lying cultivated soils survive almost intact under their blanket of blown sand.

Gauld (1981) in a survey of the soils and forestry potential of the Culbin Forest, discussed in detail the changes brought about by afforestation. He found that soil morphology, the chemical and physical properties of the sand, water table level, soil moisture content, circulation and seasonal variation of nutrients and leaching were all modified to some extent. He listed the detailed research projects carried out over the years into the effects of soil and site factors on timber growth and added that few forests in the U.K. had undergone such detailed investigations.

## DRAINAGE

The recent growth of trees in the Culbin Forest has steadily lowered the water table, and many of the small winter lochs have completely dried-up (Plate 9). The permanent ground water level as indicated by the blue-grey anaerobic sand is found nearer the surface in the poorly-drained sands in the west, but is at a greater depth in the east. Here banded horizons in the sand above this ground water level indicate that the water table has lowered by some 0.5m. This can readily be demonstrated in the Buckie Loch. On the large dunes, away from their margins, the water table is, of course, very much lower. There is, however, a little moisture retained in the sand below a thin layer of wind-blown sand at the surface. Ovington (1950) gave details of moisture distribution in various situations on the dunes.

Some 300 years ago, when the area was being farmed, the water table was much higher in the fertile estuarine soil areas than it is today, and with drainage techniques being virtually unknown in these days, considerable stretches of land which today look as though they might always have been workable, may have been left as marsh. Along the southern margin of the old Culbin estate ran a peat-filled hollow—the

Plate 9    A winter loch in the N.E. Culbin Sands before afforestation.

Logie Moss—which marked the former channel of the River Findhorn. Some parts were worked for peats and others for grazing, but it was drained only by a sluggish stream winding northeastwards towards Earnhill. Present day crop-marks highlight the probable extent of drainage problems in the fields in this area, and point to a smaller acreage being under cultiviation in the 1600s than today. In the low-lying hollow at Clay Moss silty estuarine soils with a higher clay content are found, and though possibly cultivated in places, would have been used as a source of clay for the floors of the turf houses of the old estate (fig. 27, p.131). Other peat mosses were located along the hollow at the foot of the "Bank", extending westwards to the Loch Loy area, while smaller ones occurred among the dunes between there and the coast (fig. 10, p.19, and Appendix 3). Much of the western part of the present forest was originally flat, wet carse-land with low dunes. The peaty areas, with their higher nutrient supply, have good

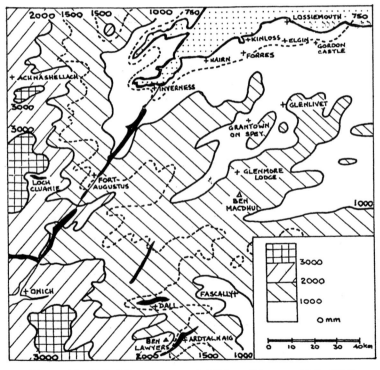

Figure 18    Rainfall—average rainfall in millimetres 1941–1970.

forestry potential, but the high water table in the poorly-drained parts has an adverse effect on both nutrient uptake and on tree stability.

At 600m per annum, the average rainfall over this part of Moray is low in comparison with surrounding areas, and when evaporation and transpiration are taken into account, the Culbin is seen to lie in a drought area in late spring and early summer (figs. 18 and 19, p.69). In the old Culbin estate, the very flat nature of the agricultural land led to a slower run-off and this coupled with the higher water table would have been advantageous in dry years. Then, as now, Lower Moray enjoyed climatic advantages from its sheltered geographical position.

# RECENT AND CONTEMPORARY CHANGE

## SAND-BLOWING IN CULBIN

Early descriptions of the sand dunes of Culbin and any associated sand-blowing problems are very scarce.

In his diary, Brodie (1863) mentioned that in April 1663 Nairn was in danger of being quite lost by the sand and the water, and in April of 1673 there was a severe drought in Dyke and Auldearn. The Rev. James Allen in September 1689 decribed getting caught in a severe sandstorm at Delnies west of Nairn. Alexander Kinnaird, the last laird of Culbin, appealed to Parliament in 1695 for tax relief as "the two best parts of his estate of Culbin, by an unevitable fatality was quite ruined and destroyed, occasioned by great and vast heaps of Sand (which had over-blown the samen) so that there was not a vestige to be seen of his manner place of Culbin, yairds, orchyairds and mains thereof and which within these twenty years were as considerable as many in the Countrey of Morray." (*Acts of Parliament Scotland*—1695, p 479). This led to an act being passed for the preservation of Meadowes, Lands and Pasturages lying adjacent to sand hills by prohibiting the pulling of Bent and Juniper. In 1698 he appealed again, this time for protection from his creditors, mentioning that by then the best three parts of his estate had been inundated.

St. John (1846) described his wanderings through these desert areas with the eye of a naturalist and his account is free from drama. Hugh Miller (1854, 1859) described the scene, concentrating on geological problems. He noted that pebbles had been pitted and polished by the action of sand-blasting in the same way as in the deserts of North Africa.

Martin (1860) in his flowery, descriptive prose, gave a detailed and dramatic account of his venturing through the dunes on a day with westerly gales, and how he was met by "such a powerful blast of wind that came sweeping round the corner of the (sand) hill, as seemed to be a work altogether beyond the common operation of nature. So violent and tormenting were those attacks, that I could not help thinking that the fairies must have leagued together to punish me for entering their domains. Whether the fairies took part in the affair or not, I am not prefered to affirm, but coming out of the gorge I felt as though a dozen thongs were lashing me with great force around the body, and I actually felt as if the points of them had reached upwards and were twitching my face. Ropes of sand are generally spoken of with a degree of contempt, but really when they operate like the thongs of Culbin, they are not to be despised". Having at last escaped from the storm, he returned again on a calm day and, in complete contrast, described the extraordinary stillness that prevailed everywhere and how all was as silent a death making him feel depressed with the awful solitude. He later mentioned that the earliest reference to sand-blowing in the Culbin was in 1676, though some pasture to the west had been covered earlier: the source of his information is not known.

Bain's descriptions of the Culbin Sands (1881, 1911, 1922 and 1928) are the most widely known and later versions were accompanied by the excellent photographs taken for the Geological Survey ca. 1910. These and later photographs certainly capture the imagination, and demonstrate the scale of the desert-like wilderness (Plates 4, 9–15). Many of the more casual descriptions of other visitors make interesting reading because of the extra snippets of information they contain.

There was quite a variety in the estimates of the maximum height of the dunes given by the early writers but most figures lay between 30 and 36m. Martin, in his first paper in 1835, described them as fully 15m high, by 1860 he had them at 30m, by 1867 fully 37m and finally in 1875 many were up to 61m in height. The dunes were mapped by Ogilvie (1923) just before the First World War and by C.A. Fisher for Steers (1937). Both showed some dunes reaching up to the order of 30m in height. Today the Ordnance Survey shows the highest as 29m. One enterprising gentleman calculated that there were 50,000,000 tons of sand in the Culbin (Murdoch 1893).

The main topic of discussion for most authors was the speed of advance of the dunes which inundated the Old Barony of Culbin in 1694, and whether there had been a gradual deterioration or a sudden over-run. When Steers presented his paper in 1937, R.A. Bagnold pointed out that from his calculations, if a wind were to blow over the area for 24 hours at an average speed of 64km per hour, and the sand which the wind carried on to the area was deposited over a depth downwind of 1.6km, the greatest thickness of sand which could be deposited would be 2.5cm. This calculation did not take into account the friction due to the sand so that this sand movement would only occur with equivalent winds in open country of 112km per hour.

Bagnold was a recognised authority on sand-blowing and had made a study of the desert sands of North Africa for many years. His textbook on the subject (Bagnold 1954) contains a wealth of information of interest to both the professional and the layman, with the basic processes being

Plate 10   A large dune advancing on a plantation in the Maviston area, 1909 (courtesy British Geological Survey).

explained in simple terms. A popular misconception regarding sandstorms is the failure to distinguish sand from dust. Fine dust from areas of soil can rise to heights of many hundreds of metres and the particles remain in suspension for considerable periods due to convection currents or turbulence. True sand drives across country as a thick low-flying cloud with a clearly-marked upper surface. The bulk of the sand movement is close to ground level and the effects of sand-blasting on rocks or posts is usually below 45cm. On a sandy beach on a windy day the moving sand is seen as a low white mist moving over the surface. Sand grains bounce along like ping-pong balls, some bouncing high off pebbles, and although the sand looks as though it is a low cloud in suspension, film taken in wind tunnel experiments shows the grains falling back at a low angle, bouncing into stationary grains, jostling them along or ejecting them into the air in turn. The process of bouncing is termed *saltation* while the bulk of the energy goes into promoting the slow forward *surface creep* of a large number of grains. Experiment shows that up to a quarter of the total volume is moved by surface creep. The cube of the wind velocity enters into the expression for sand flow, so that a single day's storm will move more sand than a month of gentle breezes.

Sand dunes advance by sand moving up the gentle rear slope by saltation and surface creep and blowing or spilling over the steepening down-wind face. When this reaches a maximum angle of 34°, the sand shears along a plane of a few degrees lesser slope and an avalanche takes place. This means that the dune advances in short jerks with each small avalanche. As the dune grows in height, the amount of sand needed to promote the avalanche increases, so that a dune 15m high in a wind of 49km per hour advances at 1.8cm per hour, while with the same wind speed over one 40cm in height, the advance is at 67cm per hour. Ovington (1950) noted that the large dune, Lady Culbin, had moved at an average rate of 6.5cm per day over a six week period.

With the rougher aspect of a pebbly area, the wind close to the surface decreases so that in light winds sand tends to accumulate in pebbly areas. With the onset of strong winds this reservoir is ready for tapping.

Along the low-lying coastal plains of Moray and Nairn considerable soil and sand blowing takes place at the present day, with roads periodically being blocked by sand and spectacular clouds of dust darkening the sky. The areas mainly giving trouble are the intensely cropped farm lands near Roseisle, Forres and Nairn. This occurs mainly in the late spring and early summer before the newly-planted crops have developed sufficiently to anchor the loose soil.

This area is one of very low rainfall—the yearly average of some 600mm is in stark contrast to the figures of over 3000mm per annum nearer the west coast (fig. 18, p.62). With the prevailing wind being strongly in the

Plate 11   Dead trees emerge as the dunes move on. Maviston area, 1909 (courtesy British Geological Survey).

southwest, the "Laich of Moray" is sheltered on three sides by the mountains. The monthly rainfall averages (fig. 19) show low rainfall in the late spring and early summer, and when evaporation and transpiration are taken into account, the soil moisture deficit can lead to drought conditions. Almost all strong winds and gales blow from the southwest and with southwesterly warm-sector winds, the Föhn effect can be very marked in lower Moray. This is a process under which warm moist air blowing against the coasts and mountains to the west produces heavy rain there as it is forced to rise, and then as it descends as a drier wind on the lee side towards the Moray Firth it rapidly warms up and the cloud breaks to give dry, warm and sunny conditions. Due to this effect, Lower Moray enjoys a better climate than almost all other places at the same latitude with only southwest Sweden being its equal. However, the higher temperatures and lower humidities combine with locally enhanced turbulent winds, and sand and dust storms frequently result.

In the days of the old Culbin estate, the pulling of marram grass and heather for thatch, animal bedding and other domestic purposes, together with the stripping of turf for house building, middens and fuel (see p.130) left large areas of bare sand exposed to these dry winds, and sand-blowing drastically increased. About 1663 Nairn Town Council issued orders forbidding anyone cutting turf at the seaside, showing there was already some alarm (Bain 1928, p.225).

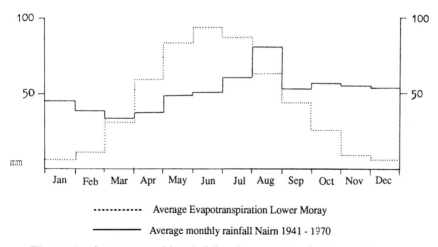

Figure 19   Average monthly rainfall and evaporation for Lower Moray.

Old blow-out patterns in larger dunes, now stabilised, are still recognisable, particularly the form of the old Maviston dunes, which were marked as landmarks as early as 1685 in Grenville Collins' coastal survey. Along the margin of the coastal strip large unplanted foredures also suffered blow-outs, but most of these have by now been eroded away. The old maps by Avery, General Roy and Peter May and the Brodie estate plan of 1770 showed that the areas with the largest dunes lay nearer the coast. Many of the dunes in the Culbin Sands show the elongated form of seif dunes running in the direction of the prevailing strong winds (fig. 20, p.71) with good examples near the forestry road between Wellhill and Binsness. As these dunes built downwind, interference with sand supplies upwind from the growth of later dunes made their progress and trend somewhat erratic. With tree-planting moving steadily across the area from the southwest to the northeast, the general supply of sand was gradually being anchored, and the whole dune movement brought to a halt.

On theoretical grounds, as put forward by Bagnold, it seems unlikely that a sudden surge of high dunes overwhelmed the old estate and all the evidence points to a gradual advance of sand, accelerated by the damage done by the stripping of the vegetation from the old shingle ridges. Under the increasing pressures of the disasterous cold climatic spell, there was little room for manoeuvre for any laird already in difficulties, let alone for one with sand-blowing added to his misfortunes. Towards the close of the century prolonged spells of poor weather led to almost complete crop failure throughout eastern Scotland in 7 out of 10 years (see pages 127–8). Some years later when sand-blowing affected the lands of Inverugie near Roseisle, the energetic laird had the sand trenched to regain the use of his lands. Whether this would have been a feasible project at Culbin with its vast reservoirs of sand, seems unlikely. Like all the stories of the Buried Barony, we have only limited hard facts to go on and we shall probably never know if the laird and his friends added anything to the tale for effect.

As with areas like the Sands of Forvie and Glenluce, there is no shortage of legends about the causes of the disaster which struck the Barony in 1694. A poem by Eisa Gordon-Cumming (1878) had the Laird chosing to play cards on the Sabbath rather than go to church, and then being trapped into playing with the Devil, while the storm raged outside: he was then doomed to play on forever. Several versions of this tale exist. Bain (1922) had the tale of the Laird having been cursed by a Fair Maid of Norway, whom he had kept in confinement. The disaster was also a judgement on the Laird for breaking the Sabbath by having his people plough, sow and reap on Sundays. Other tales are of the Laird's overhaste to have some old crones put to death for witchcraft, followed by the predictable curse. Then there were the variations on how smugglers buried their loot and could not find it again.

There are several accounts of the remains of old buildings including the manor house being temporarily exposed by storms. Some fanciful tales were attached, but the more practical observation was also made that once exposed, the ruins were quickly "quarried" by neighbouring farmers for their own use—there being no outcrops of rock anywhere in the area where building stone could be won. Some of the tales of the inundation of

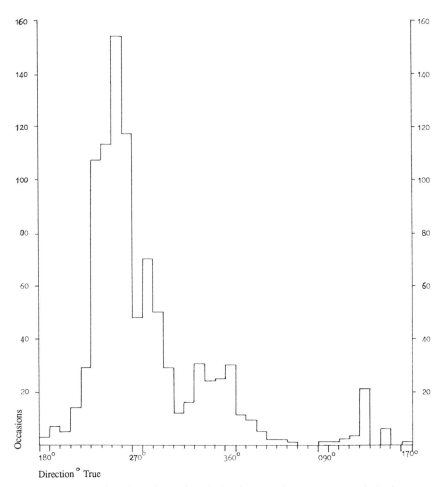

Figure 20   The direction of hourly winds of over 30kt (15m per sec.) during a 10 year period at Kinloss.

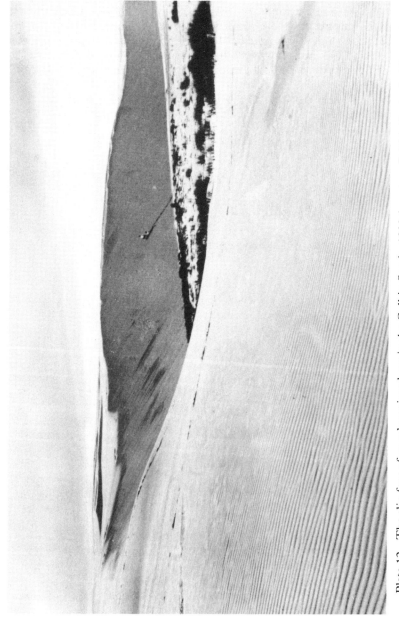

Plate 12    The slip face of an advancing dune in the Culbin Sands, 1909 (courtesy British Geological Survey).

the farmlands of the old estate are obviously false. For example, Bain (1922 p.23) describes how the storm "came suddenly and with short warning. A man ploughing had to desert his plough in the middle of the furrow. The reapers in a field of late barley had to leave without finishing their work. In a few hours the plough and the barley were buried beneath the sand." As described on p.124 *et. seq.*, farming routine was controlled by a system of ancient practices which were rigidly adhered to. Under this approach as soon as the crops were reaped the land was grazed by the animals and not ploughed till spring. (Note that the plough decribed by Bain as being exhibited in the Elgin Museum is not the one now on display: though also found at Culbin it is of a later period). The cottar-tounes of the estate were most probably situated on the edge of the rough grazing ground on the shingle ridges and could have experienced trouble before the arable ground was affected.

The scene has also been made use of by writers who wove their historical novels round the characters and landscape of the period. Perhaps the best known of these are by Maurice Walsh (1937) and Brodie Innes (1915). Both authors lived in the area and used their knowledge of local folk lore and history to good effect.

## THE STABILIZATION OF THE SANDS AND THE PLANTING OF THE CULBIN FOREST

The impressive series of some 30 photographs taken ca. 1909 for the Geological Survey, which includes Plates 10, 11, 12, 13 in this account, captures the desolation and unique splendour of the Culbin Sands prior to afforestation. This series is complemented by photographs taken by private individuals in later years, (Plates 4, 14, 15). The surviving early maps of the area, (Avery, 1730: Roy, 1755· May, 1758) give few details other than the outline of the waste-land, but a plan of Brodie Estates dating from 1770 contains many small details and notes on the western half of the Culbin (fig. 10, p.19). Additional information on the former landscape can be gleaned from various written descriptions of aspects of the Culbin, though many are simply repeated from earlier accounts. Looking at the 28sq km of forest today, it is difficult to believe that it is the same place.

The first efforts to reclaim the sandy wastelands by planting trees were made by R. Grant of Kincorth in 1837. He was not looking for profit, but was attempting to improve the appearance of his estate as well as providing shelter for the arable land by planting belts of Scots pine and some broad-leaved trees. This operation was gradually extended over the 28ha. of Kincorth covered by sand, and by 1865 there was a thriving plantation of

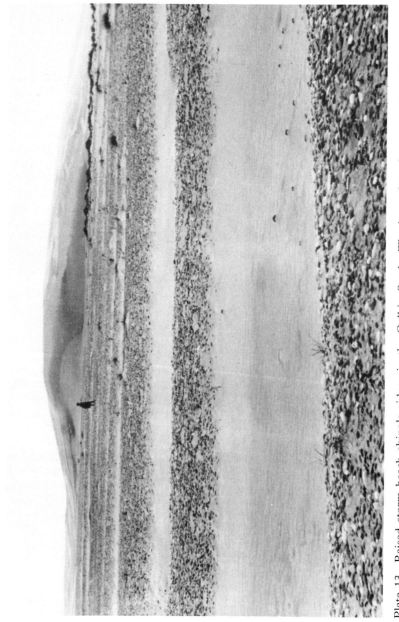

Plate 13   Raised storm beach shingle ridges in the Culbin Sands. The large dune known as Lady Culbin in the background, 1909 (courtesy British Geological Survey).

Scots pine and larch (Grigor, 1881). John Grigor, a nurseryman from Forres, also relates how he planted 80ha. of Scots pine and larch on the neighbouring sand-covered lands of Moy estate in 1840 and a further 40ha. two years later. It is interesting to note that he described how the Scots pine continued to grow when drifted up with sand, so long as a year or two's growth remained above the surface. He also pointed out that larch would not grow on the shingle ridges and that the Scots pine growing there "assumed a yellowish-green colour and were much more dwarfish than those on pure sand". He observed that where peat underlay the sand, tree growth was much better and that trenching the ground was advantageous to growth. He recommended using thinnings of brushwood for thatching the sand to check drifting and to shelter young trees, quoting methods used in similar tracts of country along the Gulf of Gascony in France as early as 1789. All these points were to re-emerge 100 years later.

Some 100ha. of trees planted in the 1860s suffered badly from being over-run by rabbits. Writing in 1846, Charles St. John, in discussing the rabbit population of the sands, had said "Whatever the rabbits and hares feed on, they are larger there than in the more cultivated and fertile parts

Plate 14    The size of the dunes in the Culbin Sands fired the imagination, c.1938.

Plate 15    A group from Forres, including Maurice Walsh, on a walk in the Culbin.

of the county." In the 1880s plantations were sucessfully established at Binsness and on Brodie estates, so that by 1900 just over 1200ha. of trees were flourishing. Small additions followed, and during the First World War logging took place over the whole area, but there was also an extensive forest fire.

The private estate owners obviously did not have the resources to stabilise the whole dune area and the northern and northeastern sectors remained untouched. The newly-formed Forestry Commission took an interest in the problem. This organisation had been established in 1919 and part of its remit was to increase the production of home-grown timber, to make use of waste and marginal land and to improve rural employment. Starting in 1922 the Commission began purchasing "The Culbin" from the estates of Moy, Binsness, Dalvey, Brodie and Loch Loy. The first 10 years were taken up by replanting the felled areas which totalled 915ha., and in the following decade another 285ha. were planted, including the first major attempt to plant the dunes. Another large fire necessitated a replanting programme in 1939 which was interrupted when the Culbin was taken over as a military training area. Reminders of the latter period resurface in the form of unexploded shells and rockets, and in the mid 1980s several hundreds of unexploded rockets were recovered from the northern coastal strip during a concerted effort by bomb disposal teams. Planting started again in 1946 and by 1963 a further 1500ha. had been completed, bringing the total forest area up to the 2560ha. we see today.

The exercise was not without its problems, particularly in stabilising the dunes. The accepted method of anchoring sand was the planting of marram grass (Ammophila arenaria) which is a tough, long-stemmed grass which spreads wandering roots under the surface (Plate 16). On these root-clusters form, from which new leaf-shoots propagate to the surface. The result is thick clumps of sturdy grass, with stems up to a metre in length and supplied by an interconnected network of root-systems. The grass is drought- and salt-resistant. Its main advantage is that it raises the boundary layer above the sand when the wind blows: creating a region of calm air at the surface. The sand grains are therefore not so easily set in motion. When covered by blowing sand the grass grows up through the new cover, maintained by roots tapping the moisture well below. The roots are strong enough to hold together to some extent when uncovered during a minor blow-out, but disintegrate under more severe conditions.

The grass spreads naturally by wind-blown seeds as well as by wandering shoots, and can be transplanted by pulling root tufts from mature clumps and planting them in small holes This method was used in the Culbin to establish an anchoring network of marram over the sand. The tufts, planted in rows spaced 0.8m apart (Plate 16) were left to grow for three years before planting commenced. It was found that the process worked well on the flatter ground, but on the more exposed, open sand dunes the effect was not sufficient to anchor the dunes, particularly in gusty conditions, and the damage done to the root systems during blow-outs was greater than expected. After a 10 year trial period, the thatching of the dunes with brushwood was introduced (we cannot say invented) and this proved to be the answer in creating a deeper blanket of still air at the surface. Thinnings from other forests were brought in for the purpose and up to 100 tonnes per hectare were used (Plates 17 and 18). The stems, still with the leaves and needles, were laid down with their butts towards the prevailing wind, so as to completely blanket the sand. The trees were planted through this thatch and left to grow up through it as it gradually decayed. This decayed matter supplied a small but valuable quantity of humus to the surface soil and a minute but critically important amount of mineral nutrients (Edlin, 1976).

Trees were planted at 1.4m spacings, which came out at some 5000 trees per hectare. The policy was to start planting in the southwest and gradually work towards the northeast so that, as successive plots were stabilised, the trees there would provide shelter for the younger ones planted in their lee.

Plate 16    Planting trees among marram grass tufts on the dunes, c.1948.

Plate 17  Collecting thinnings for thatch, c.1948.

Plate 18   Spreading thatch on the dunes, c.1948.

Progress was therefore deliberately set at a modest rate, and by 1954 the last of the open northeast sector was covered (fig. 21, p.85 and Plate 19). As the trees grew they provided their own protection from the wind, replacing the deteriorating thatch and also contributing their own litter to the forest soil. Just how critical the conditions were is illustrated by the fact that at the intersections of forest rides, where the surface was exposed to winds from additional directions, the patches of bare sand took many years longer to cover over. Overall, 32 years were devoted to planting the 2560ha.

Experience in other areas indicated that, with the low rainfall conditions enjoyed in this most favoured part of Scotland, the only type of tree likely to survive on this sandy coastal strip would be some species of pine. Of the hardwoods, only birch would prove successful on the poor soils. The success that the early private landowners had had with native Scots pine (pinus sylvestris) has been echoed by that type now occupying 65% of the forest. On the higher dunes the choice has been the Corsican Pine (P. nigra, var maritima), occupying 30% of the forest, and this has also proved a success in spite of being adversely affected by frost. This species was

Plate 19    Aerial view of the N.E. corner of the Culbin Sands in 1947 before afforestation (courtesy Cambridge University Collection: copyright reserved).

Plate 20    Pines planted near Binsness around 1900 just keeping their heads above the sand in 1948 (from *The Buried Barony* by A. A. Macgregor publ. Robert Hale Limited with permission).

first introduced at Binsness by Major Chadwick at the turn of the century, and one fine stand remains to demonstrate the productivity of the species. Here the trees were planted on the old agricultural soils of the former Easter Binn estate, prior to the encroachment of the larger dunes, and managed to keep their heads above the advancing sand (Plate 20). Afforestation gradually halted the advance of the dunes and today we see a stand of mature trees some 21m tall, many of which are enclosed in sand for up to half of their height.

Normally a tree trunk tapers evenly upwards, but these broaden upwards to a maximum at the sand surface and then taper off upwards in the normal fashion. The stand was thinned about 1980 and it was decided to conserve the remainder. It is apparent that the half-enclosed trees are now more exposed to wind blow, and are moving appreciably in their "sockets" of sand. One trunk has been excavated by the Forestry Commission and can be studied at NGR (NJ 0215 6370) (Plate 21). The Geological Survey photographs of 1910 show the effects of very large dunes having completely engulfed mature trees, and dead trunks are shown emerging at a later date from the trailing edges of the dunes (Plates 10 and 11).

Trials with planting other types of tree met with varied results. The maritime pine (P. pinaster) from the Mediterranean and the Monterey pine (P. radiata) from California had clearly been taken outside their climatic range. The lodgepole pine (P. contorta) was tried because it was native to the coasts of British Columbia. Although it proved highly successful, it only occupies some 2% of the forest, but the trials contributed to the widespread use of the species in upland areas. Douglas fir, Norway spruce and Grand fir were also planted during the trials, but not selected for general use, while European and Japanese larch were miserable failures. The Species Trial Plots in which all these various types were planted have been preserved, and the now mature trees can be examined at (NH 991 608).

Today, what started as a protection forest planted on sand, has moved on to become a fully productive and profitable unit producing some 13,000 cubic metres of cut timber per annum. Many thousands of transmission and telegraph poles are supplied as well as timber for pulping, fibreboard, pallets and saw-logs. Large areas have been clear-felled and replanted, using the knowledge accumulated over the years.

The story does not end there because the Culbin Forest is also a field research station of national importance. Experimental work looking into all aspects of nutrition deficiency is carried out, and here there is close co-operation between the Forestry Commission's research outstation at Newton Nurseries near Elgin and the Macaulay Institute for Soil Research in Aberdeen. Experimental plots have been set up in the forest and some sites have been earmarked for extended rotations and conservation. Since

Plate 21    Excavation of one of the trees in plate 20 shows it to have developed a
reversed taper (1990).

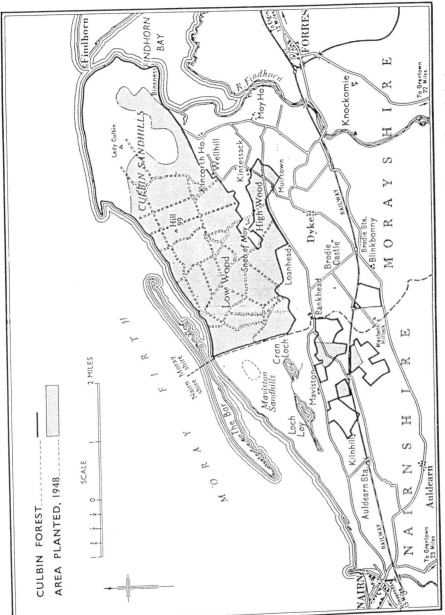

Figure 21  The Culbin Forest and its surroundings in 1948 (courtesy Forestry Commission).

no retention can be permanent, certain stands such as the Species Trial Plots will be preserved for their natural life, while others such as the coastal fringe, will probably never be clear-felled.

A most interesting plot is the "Deficiency Garden" in the northeast corner of the forest at (NJ 026 640). Here, where the almost bare shingle ridges offer the most nutrient-starved areas in the whole of the Culbin, the experimental application of selected fertilizers under conrolled conditions highlights the importance of the regular application of nitrogenous fertilizers when planting on sandy soils. The results are startling, and in the plots, trees over 30 years old, which were deprived of nitrogen, stand barely one metre high, in stark contrast with their healthy, "well-fed" brothers nearby (Plate 22). Today the careful application of fertilizer of the correct type at the correct stage in growth has led to a dramatic increase in timber yield.

Progeny testing and the continuing development of the national seed-bank are controlled from Newton. In spite of the commerical success of the forest, investigations into improving methods of planting and the selection of the best species of tree for various localities continue. Field research by the Macaulay Institute also goes ahead with further nitrogen cycle investigations where the growth of young trees planted in clear-felled areas is monitored to determine second rotation nutrition needs for optimum growth.

Accounts of the afforestation of the Culbin Sands are to be found in Ovington (1950) and Edlin (1976). As well a giving historical details, they discuss changes to the flora, microflora, soil-profiles and chemistry, and the moisture distribution as the forest developed. Physical changes in the sand dunes under tree crops of different species and ages are dealt with by Wright (1955) and he also gives an account (1956) of the changes in the distribution of major nutrients in the profiles on the same sites. Gauld (1981) looks at the forestry potential of the various sections of the forest from the point of view of the soils. Other less detailed accounts are given by Annand (1936), Steven (1936), Forestry Commission (1950) and Scott (1975b).

## A SITE OF SPECIAL SCIENTIFIC INTEREST

As well as being of outstanding interest to foresters, the Culbin has, over the years, played host to archaeologists, botanists, ornithologists, geomorphologists, field clubs, school parties etc., in great numbers; most of whom might already have been stimulated by the romance and legends of the sands, before coming to pursue their particular interests. With such a wealth of "-ologies" in one area, it seems only proper that the whole

Plate 22   A 35 year old Scots Pine planted on the shingle ridge, stunted by lack of nitrogen.

forest should have been designated a Site of Special Scientific Interest, (SSSI).

## ARCHAEOLOGY

Early writers on the Culbin tended to dismiss archaeological relics found in the sands as being of little interest, mentioning pottery fragments, bits of iron and brass, stone whorls, flint arrowheads and chips "belonging to a period much more remote than the historic days of Culbin" (Martin, 1860). In a later lecture, Martin (1875) gave a more extensive list of finds, but by this time archaeologists had been investigating the area. Linton (1877) gave details of discoveries he had made in 1874, and was followed by Mathewson (1878) describing his investigations of two years later. A detailed archaeological examination of the Culbin was made on behalf of the *Royal Society of Antiquities* by Black (1891). He investigated shell middens from both ancient and more recent times, finding many artefacts near these sites. From his descriptions, some of his exavations were made through the mounds which were the small remnants of "butte dunes".

He described the discovery of several cinerary urns and gave an illustration of one which was the tallest ever found in Scotland. Perhaps the most interesting finds were from a site where articles of bronze had been manufactured, and had earlier been described by Linton (1877). These included bronze axe heads and the stone moulds used in their manufacture, together with a large variety of pins, buckles, tweezers, rivets, rings, chains, fish-hooks, brooches and other ornaments. Black also included an illustration of a magnificent bronze armlet found earlier in the century. Glass beads and ornaments of various types were described, and over 200 pieces of jet—mostly fragments of broches, necklaces and rings— were among the finds. The many types of flint artefacts he described and illustrated included arrowheads, spearheads, knives, saws, and scrapers. Stone implements found were axes, hammer-stones, whorls, saddle-querns and a cup made of steatite. He stated that finds from Culbin already in the National Collection included over 4000 flint scrapers, more than 1000 arrow- and spearheads of flint, and some 80 strike-a-light and gun flints. Coins of various ages and broches of silver and enamel were also being discovered during this period. The Catalogues of the *National Museum of Antiquities* (1892 a & b) list some of the specimens from the Culbin Sands which had been donated or purchased and others which were on display (Plates 23, 24).

The Rev. McEwan of Dyke had by this time begun making his extensive collection, which was later dispersed. Part of it was donated to the Forres Museum, where today only a small part survives. From this period up to the time the forest was fully planted, a Sunday walk to the Culbin "to search for arrows" was a popular pastime for the local people. The result was that a very large number of finds were made and went unrecorded, and these small private collections simply disappeared. On the other hand, at the same time many more found their way to the National Museums, and before vanishing into the vaults, they were, at least, recorded. Today the National Museum of Scotland holds over 29,500 items from Culbin, mostly flint artefacts. (Ian Morrison, personal communication). Small collections can be seen in the museums in Elgin and Forres.

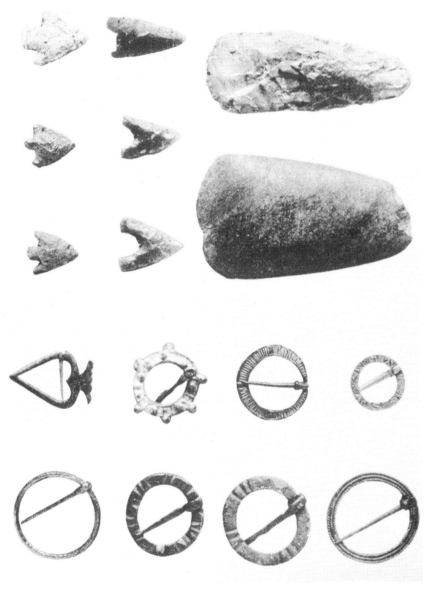

Plate 23   Artefacts found in the Culbin Sands (from *The Buried Barony* by A. A.
Macgregor publ. Robert Hale Limited with permission).

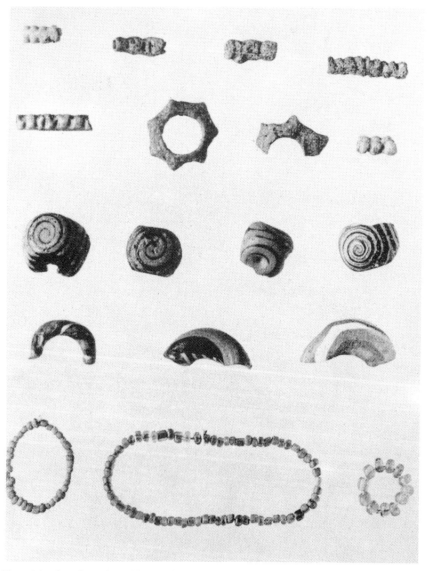

Plate 24    Artefacts found in the Culbin Sands (from *The Buried Barony* by A. A. Macgregor publ. Robert Hale Limited with permission).

Callander (1911), after describing fresh finds of clay utensils, made an interesting comparison between the artefacts found in the Culbin Sands and those found in the Glenluce Sands in southwest Scotland. Various accounts of visits made by private individuals or on organised excursions over the years, occasionally yield details of finds not recorded elsewhere. Murray (1921b) showed the Moray Field Club some foundation stones which were believed to mark the site of some of the outbuildings belonging to the old Mansion house of Culbin, and stated that this was the spot where two local gentlemen had recently found sandstone blocks bearing the coats of arms of the Kinnaird and the Inneses. Anderson (1938) gave what may have been the last recording of the site of the foundation stones of the old mansion, stating that they were then fully exposed. His notes include descriptions of the various objects he had collected over the many years he had been visiting the Culbin and part of his collection is now in the Forres Museum. The lantern slides, with which he illustrated his talks, show himself and friends enjoying their Sunday walks (Plates 4, 14, 15).

The most recent accounts of excavations in the Culbin Sands were those given by Coles and Taylor (1970). They examined the contents of a kitchen midden, and from the shells, bone-fragments, seeds and other objects found, built up a picture of the diet of the inhabitants in those far-off days. They considered that the site was a hut encampment of a temporary nature and obtained a radio-carbon dating of 3300 BP from a layer of carbonised wood. The site was near the western end of the shingle promontory which forms the backbone of the Culbin Foreland, and at the time of occupation would have been near the mouth of the river which in those days flowed westwards along the south flank of the Culbin.

Not all shell middens are of great antiquity, and the inhabitants of the old Culbin estate and neighbouring properties no doubt frequently had to forage for shellfish to supplement their meagre diet, especially in famine years. (A necessary practice in winter in the more remote islands of west and north Scotland, even into the second half of the present century). The kitchen middens contain a lot of shell material, the main species being: edible cockle (Cerastoderma edule), edible mussel (Mytilus edulis), common periwinkle (Littorina littorea) and razorshell (Ensis ensis). Some fragments of crab claws and fish and animal bones have also been recorded. Mathewson (1878) stated that shell middens were found in great numbers along the northern edge of the shingle ridges. These may have been near temporary shelters for the salmon fishers along the old river bank prior to the change of course in 1701. A problem arises here and at the site of the Hill of Findhorn, due to the proximity of the mussel scalps in the estuary, which provided the bait for the white fish boats from that community, and where one would expect extensive dumps of mussel shells.

Most of the objects found in the Culbin were discovered on the shingle ridges, which provided a firm surface on to which anything dropped on to the sand surface would settle once the sand blew away. Even if again covered by drifting sand, the object would remain in that spot, perhaps to be uncovered at a later date. A few artefacts were also found on the old agricultural areas, where the firm surface of the compacted soil formed a stable base to support them when the dunes moved on.

Today the stabilised sand no longer moves off to expose fresh ground and any object that may lie there. That era of discovery has come to a close without anyone uncovering to oft-quoted smugglers' hoard which legend records as having been lost under the shifting dunes. The sand does, however, occasionally give up secrets of a different sort, and in 1986 the wreckage of a crashed aircraft was re-discovered after having lain forgotten for over 40 years and further finds of unexploded shells and rockets along the north coastal margin may prove to be of archaeological interest to future generations.

The diversity of the objects of archaeological interest discovered in the Culbin spans the entire history of Moray from the time of the hunter-gatherers to the present day. It is hoped that, before long, with the use of the improved dating tehniques now available, a more detailed time scale of the past occupation of the whole area will emerge.


# BOTANY

We are fortunate in having had in the district a botanist of international standing who devoted most of her life to the study of the flora of Moray and who had a special interest in the Culbin Sands.

Mary McCallum Webster was *the* authority on the plant life of the Culbin, and as well as giving us a concise account of her findings, she listed those of the many enthusiasts, specialists and learned societies who had examined the area at first hand since the earliest collections were made by James Brodie of Brodie towards the end of the 18th century. Her books contains a full check list of the flora of Culbin, summaries of the botanical exploration of Culbin, sketches of the chief characters involved and a useful bibliography. (Webster 1968, 1978).

Her synopsis of the changes in the flora during the development of the forest reads as follows:

"Following afforestation, the ecological succession is rapid and often telescoped, thus communities may be impermanent. Important changes take place. Acrocarpous mosses and lichens begin to colonise, and with a build up of humus from the accumulation of leaf litter and the lowering of the water table, the surface profile commences. Pleurocarpous mosses become dominant and as the tree canopy heightens, a rich vascular flora creeps in. In certain moist areas, such plants as Pyrola minor, Orthilia secunda, Moneses uniflora, Goodyera repens, Listera cordata and Corallorhiza trifida become abundant, but owing to thinning and felling of the pines, are never permanent. Calluna vulgaris, Carex arenaria, Agrostis tenuis and Holcus lanatus invade the plantations, and the former plants are choked out to find more suitable habitats. With the maturity of the forest and the drying out of the dune depressions by draining, the making of new roads etc., a gradual change in the flora is taking place, the main trends being a reduction in numbers and importance of dune slack and marsh species and a corresponding increase in forest species and arable weeds".

The individual papers written by visiting botantists give more detailed accounts of the changes that took place in the various habitats over the years, and these are also of interest to the non-specialist as they contain descriptions of the area before afforestation which are not available elsewhere. Viz: Ewing (1912), Burgess (1920), Stewart and Patton (1923, 1924), Patton and Stewart (1923). Later descriptions overlap into the realms of forestry and are discussed under that heading.

Salt-resistant grasses and plants have colonised the stretches of bare sand between the Old Bar and the Culbin to form a large expanse of saltings: a process which probably began even before the bar was severed in 1701. The flat-lying carse land on which the western parts of the forest stand were, in part, developed in this way. The saltings south of the centre of the Old Bar, where development is most mature, was mapped as dry land on the most recent Ordnance Survey maps. Unfortunately this stretch is being actively eroded and slabs of fine layered soils up to 35cm thick are exposed on the beach on the seaward side of the bar as it advances landwards over these old saltings. (Ross 1979E, 1987E). The fragile green carpet, under which a thin soil slowly forms, is easily damaged and wheel tracks in the drier portions are enlarged by sand-blowing—a process likely to continue as salmon fishing is replaced by commercial shell fish harvesting. The saltings, which are dotted with salt-pans and criss-crossed by creeks and tunnels, make ideal feeding and resting grounds for wildfowl.

The 40ha. stretch of sand in the shelter of the spit between the Buckie Loch and Jenny Rait's Hillock has been completely colonised in the very short period of some 30 years, with the plants spreading out across the bare sand at the rate of 10–15m per year. Common saltmarsh grass and creeping bent came first, raising the surface by forming a mat, then followed sea milkwort, sea pinks, sea spurry, red fescue and sea plantains.

Morrison (1976) assessed the spread of vegetation on the still mobile western half of the Old Bar by dividing it into seven sectors of differing stability and maturity. These were the unstable and stable shingle, partially-fixed and fixed dunes, dune heath, scrub, and the parts of the saltings inside the shingle recurves. He outlined the problems of fitting a pattern of succession where interruptions by factors such as erosion and inundation could halt a succession, leading to the first colonisers being reinstated at a later date, while seeds from older communities elsewhere could disrupt the logical sequence. He found that in spite of the comparative youth of the shingle ridges forming the western end, a large variety of vegetation had become established, and here too the speed at which the plants had spread over the bare sand and shingle was quite surprising. In his north-south profile across the ridges he noted that the continuous low cover of heather was replaced on the sheltered inland side, where there was a thicker cover of blown sand, by scrub up to 1.5m tall on a carpet of moss and grasses with some clumps of rank heather. These present day changes give us an insight into how the original bar and emerging estuary were colonised some 5000 years ago.

The Buckie Loch is a feature which is shown on a map of 1858 (Appendix 9) as developing in a portion of the former channel of the River Findhorn in the shelter of a hooked spit. The steady colonisation by plants of this area which was once a bare sandy stretch has been meticulously recorded, and in 1978, at the time Mary McCallum Webster published her "Flora", the Buckie Loch was still regarded as a botanist's paradise, and had the richest flora in the forest. The loch was then drying up and coarse grasses were spreading in, to the exclusion of the more exotic species. It was in that year that the sea made its first inroads into the forest, flooding through the trees for a distance of 150m just east of the loch (fig. 7, p.15). The margin of sand between the loch and the beach was being steadily eroded, and in 1983, during a severe northerly gale, the sea broke through and flooded the loch. The head of the beach is now established inside the loch margin and it is only a matter of time before the whole stretch is washed away and the saltings to the west exposed to attack (Ross 1983E). A substantial area of trees was killed off by the action of the salt water, and was subsequently cleared, while the unaffected trees on the low ground then under threat were also felled (Plate 25). The flooding in of salt water on this, and later occasions has radically reduced the variety of plant life of the loch site.

Mosses and lichens, which make low demands on the environment are abundant in the forest, and some of the mosses appeared almost as soon as the surface sand ceased to move, helping to fix it by forming close mats on the surface. These moss-mats persist through all stages of the forest growth, and in some cases the lichens become equally abundant, with the ground cover consisting almost entirely of moss and lichens plus the forest litter, and with no higher plants in evidence (Edlin 1976). Lichens are extremely sensitive to the presence of sulphur dioxide in the atmosphere and their rich carpets on the forest floor and thick streamers adorning the

Plate 25   Trees which are well down the beach outside the Buckie Loch in 1991 were 40 metres in from the coast 20 years ago.

trunks and branches are unknown in the polluted air of the industrial south.

The Culbin Sands is considered to be one of the top four sites for saxicolous lichens in the British Isles. This is brought about by the combination of a substrate that is nutrient-poor but stable, and the sheltered locality. The British Lichenological Society and the Royal Botanic Gardens, who are very interested in the site, have identified it as being the nearest thing in the botantical world to the lichen-rich pine forests of northern Norway, where stunted trees provide the right degree of shelter and not too much shade. It is the only well-developed example of this in the British Isles. In some areas of the forest lichens in spectacular clumps provide up to 90% of the ground cover. The variety is amazing, there being several hundreds of species, some of which are found nowhere else in the U.K. The richest areas occur on the eastern end of the shingle ridges near Findhorn Bay and at the western end of the shingle on the large shingle fan.

Fungi too are abundant, and according to the *British Mycological Society*, there are an exceptional number of varieties. There is some debate as to how many types might have been introduced from elsewhere with the thatching. Edlin (1976) discusses how certain species form an intimate associate with specific tree types.


## WILD LIFE

Descriptions by early writers stressed the marked absence of life amongst the dunes, though rabbits and foxes seemed to thrive (St. John, 1846). Today the Culbin houses a fairly typical selection of forest animals, including: Roe deer, Fox, Red squirrel, Brown hare, Rabbit, Badger, Stoat, Weasel, Vole, Shrew, Wood mouse, Mole and Bat, while the common seal and its pups regularly pull out on the coast. However it is usually the lone observer who sees the shy forest animals as they slip quietly away on the noisy approach of large groups who remark on their absence.

Among the birds of the Culbin, Capercaillie, Crested tit, Blue tit, Coal tit, Great tit, Cross-bill, Hoodie crow, Buzzard, Pheasant and Woodpigeon are commonly seem, while various migrants are met with in winter. One of the more unusual recordings is that of Pallas's sand grouse which nested in the Culbin Sands in 1890, the first time the bird was known to have bred in this country. In Findhorn Bay, along the coast and on the saltings, sea birds are abundant. These include all the common ducks, geese, gulls, terns and waders, as well as rare visitors. Up to a few years ago a large heronry flourished in a mature part of the forest about 1 km NW of

Binsness, but was deserted when the stand was thinned. Though some herons now nest nearer the coast, they are not so numerous as before. An interesting sight in summer is that of ospreys fishing in Findhorn Bay. All these birds attract both the resident population of ornithologists and other members of this species from farther afield. Wildfowlers are also attracted to Findhorn Bay and the saltings in increasing numbers and the establishment of a bird reserve in Findhorn Bay and the acquisition of the Old Bar by the RSPB may influence this influx in due course.

The forest also maintains a rich insect fauna, some members of which are very destructive to pine trees. The main species are Pine weevils (the most destructive), Pine looper moth, Black pine beetle, Pine shoot beetle and Pine saw fly. Damage to the trees can become so serious that the pests have to be controlled by means of aerial spraying with insecticides. There are quarantine regulations in force requiring bark to be peeled off logs before they leave the forest so that breeding beetles are not transported elsewhere, while the stumps of newly felled trees are treated to stop the spread of a fungus—Fomes annosus.

The large hills built by the Red wood ant are commonly met with in the forest, some of them of considerable size (Plate 26). Perhaps the most entertaining of the studies of insect life in the Culbin is that of the foraging parties of ants spreading out in all directions from their anthills along "highways" which they keep cleared of forest litter. Several species of butterflies brighten the picture and spiders occur in greater numbers than in any other Scottish forest.

Some studies of various animals, birds and insects have been undertaken in the forest, but with few published results.

## CONSERVATION

The Forestry Commission, being a major landowner controlling some 1.2 million ha., has had to keep abreast of the increasing demand for countryside recreation of every sort, while proceeding with its economic and social objectives. Car parks, picnic areas and facilities for short walks have been set up in most areas, meeting the requirements of most day visitors. In addition the Commission has established visitor centres, forest parks, holiday centres and camping and caravan sites. The Countryside Acts dictate that in undertaking such projects, care must be taken to conserve the natural beauty and amenity of the countryside. The common policy in all of these is that access to the forests is for walkers only.

A problem arose when, due to the distances involved, the question was raised of access by car to the magnificent sandy beaches of Culbin. It is well known that motorists are extremely reluctant to stray far from their

Plate 26   A wood ant's nest in the Culbin Forest

cars, and that any concentration of them on such a fragile beach site would inevitably lead to erosional problems. The decision was taken to establish a picnic site on Commission property in the centre of the 10km long sandy beach of Burghead Bay, not far to the east, with access to a large car park through the Roseisle Forest. This "sacrificial lamb" proved highly successful and has become one of the most popular sites in Moray, removing the threat of unrestricted access to the Culbin. Access from the sea cannot be controlled and there have been fires in the coastal parts of the forest, stemming from barbecues on the beaches. Another source of damage of a different sort is the use of the dune areas in the forest as practice grounds for "cross-country" motorcylists, whose activities plough up the thin layers of vegetation on the forest floor.

The Forestry Commission is aware of the increasing interest being taken in environmental issues and has set up Local Consultative Panels with members drawn from interested organisations in each district. The main aim of the panels is to exchange information about the present work of the Forestry Commission in the particular areas, in the fields of wildlife, conservation and recreation and to establish plans for their future development within Forestry Commission lands, taking into consideration the interests and concerns of the outside bodies and drawing on their expertise where appropriate.

Remembering that the primary objectives of the Forestry Commission in the Culbin are the efficient production of timber and continuity of the comprehensive research programme, it can be said that the SSSI has enjoyed a very considerable degree of protection for many years, and that with the continued implementation of conservation policies, the preservation of this unique area is assured.

# THE BARONY OF CULBIN
## (The popular version)

With a history going back to the beginning of the 13th century, the estate of Culbin was the finest and the most fertile in Moray. In the centre of it stood the mansion house—a large square building of dressed stones, embowered with a beautiful garden, a fruitful orchard, and a spacious lawn. It was, as we may easily believe from the social position of the Baron, and the great wealth the family undoubtedly possessed, a centre of the culture and refinement of the time.

The estate itself was called the garden and granary of Moray. "Stretching away in the distance in every direction were to be seen the highly cultivated fields with heavy corn; the rich meadows, dotted here and there with thriving herds; and the extensive pastures with numerous flocks". There were in all 3600 acres. To the east and west were 16 fair sized farms and farm houses, each tenant paying on average £200 Scots in money, as well as 40 bolls each of wheat, bere, oats and oatmeal in kind. There were numerous small crofts and huts all over the estate. The rent roll still exists.

The river Findhorn flowed past the north side of the lands in a slow, broad stream. Along its banks were rows of fishermen's huts, with their boats and fishing gear in front—all of these dwellings teeming with life and activity. The salmon fishing was particularly valuable, and the little community appears to have enjoyed a large measure of prosperity.

The late frost or protracted drought might destroy the crops in other parts of the district, but so rich and deep was the alluvial soil of Culbin that their crops never failed. One year a heavy crop of barley was reaped, though no rain had fallen since it was sown.

The great sand drift came from the west in the autumn of 1694: it came suddenly and with short warning. A man ploughing had to desert his plough in the middle of a furrow. The reapers in a field of late barley had to leave without finishing their work. In a few hours the plough and barley were buried beneath the sand. The drift, like a mightly river, came on steadily and ruthlessly, grasping field after field, and enshrouding every object in a mantle of sand. In terrible gusts the wind carried the sand amongst the dwelling houses of the people, sparing neither the hut of the cottar nor the mansion of the laird. The splendid orchard, the beautiful lawn, all shared the same fate.

In the morning after the first night of drift, the people had to break through the back of their houses to get out. They relieved the cattle and drove them to a place of safety. After a lull, the storm began again with renewed violence, and they had to flee for their lives, taking with them only such things as they could carry.

To add to the horrors of the scene, the sand choked the mouth of the river Findhorn, which now poured its flooded waters amongst the fields and homesteads, accumulating in lakes and pools till it rose to a height by which it was able to burst the barrier to the north, and find a new outlet to the sea, in its course sweeping to destruction the old village of Findhorn.

On returning, the people of Culbin were spellbound. Not a vestige, not a trace of their houses was to be seen. Everything had disappeared beneath the sand. From that time to this, the estate of Culbin has been completely buried by the sand. A portion of the old mansion house appeared about a hundred years later, like a ghostly spectre amidst the sand, and became an object of superstitious interest to the people of the neighbourhood, especially as one man who had bawled down the chimney, heard a voice distinctly respond to his cry. It eventually disappeared as suddenly as it came on the scene. Fruit trees have actually come out and blossomed and borne fruit in this sandy desert, only again to be swallowed up. The dovecote and chapel also reappeared, and their ruins supplied stones for neighbouring farm buildings.

As for the laird and his family, the sequel is more pathetic. Kinnaird escaped the night of the catastrophe with his wife and child, attended by a nurse. Their boy was but a few months old. Kinnaird petitioned Parliament to be exempt from the payment of land tax, on account of the greater part of his land being overrun by the sand and the remainder threatened. Shortly afterwards we find him forced to sell out and applying for personal protection against his creditors. Both the laird and his wife died a few years later. The faithful nurse took the child to Edinburgh, and supported him and herself by needlework.

The estate had been sold in 1698 and Kinnaird died within three months of the sale.

# THE EXTENT OF THE OLD BARONY OF CULBIN

No maps exist which show the boundaries of the old Culbin estate, and over the years many legends have grown up about the size and wealth of the Barony. In its heyday it is popularly believed to have comprised 16 farms covering 3600 acres (1457ha.) of fertile farmland and to have been the granary of Moray (e.g. Bain, 1911). Judging by a much-quoted rental for 1693 (Appendix 10), the lands would appear to have been exceptionally productive, yielding rents unparalleled in Moray, and in fact in Scotland: all this before everything was buried beneath the advancing sand dunes in 1694, and the Laird, heavily in debt, was hounded to an early grave by his creditors.

While the present writer was engaged in an investigation into the coastal processes which had formed the Culbin Foreland (p.32), it became obvious that a considerable discrepancy existed between the accepted extent of the old estate and the most generous estimate that could be made on the ground of the area of potentially arable land. This stretch had originally developed as emerging estuarine flats enclosed by a low promontory in the form of a hooked shingle spit. Details of the latter can be followed in the Culbin forest, and when mapped to scale (fig. 22, p.123) this outline and the lower reaches of the River Findhorn form boundaries which define the maximum area of the estuarine soils.

Near its mouth, the course of the River Findhorn has changed periodially during major floods, and in a dispute over fishing rights (*Court of Session* 1760) witnesses described how in its lowest reaches some 40 years earlier the river had flowed about 1200m to the east of the 1760 position. From the detailed maps by Peter May in 1758 and 1765 which were produced for the case, the most likely point for the river to have broken away from its old channel is at a point just east of Moy. From the extent of the mapped carse land, marked as periodically flooded, this would not materially affect the estimate of the extent of the arable lands to the west of the river. Accordingly, as a first estimate, there was a maximum area of 548ha. of soil available, but this would have to be shared between several farms, some not belonging to the Culbin estate.

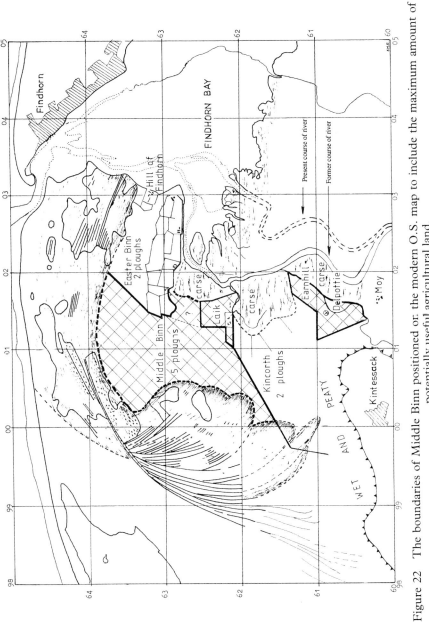

Figure 22    The boundaries of Middle Binn positioned on the modern O.S. map to include the maximum amount of potentially useful agricultural land.

Looking again at what had been written about the estate, the earliest accounts of the Kinnairds of Culbin is a brief summary by R. Grant of Kincorth which appeared as appendix LV to Shaw's *History of Moray* (1827), but the author confined himself to family affairs and scarcely mentioned the property. Much of the information about the estate, which later writers were to expound upon, was contained in C. Fraser-Mackintosh's *The Lost House of Culbin*, published in 1865. The author, a solicitor in Inverness and later Member of Parliament, was a keen historian and had received from Capt. E. Dunbar Dunbar of Seapark, Kinloss in Moray "a mass of papers connected with the estate" from which he built up a history of the Kinnaird family. Attempts to trace what happened to these papers have met with little success and although Fraser-Mackintosh bequeathed his books to Inverness Library, there is no record of any documents having been included. Similarly, on the Dunbar Dunbar side, family wills reveal nothing.

Writing in 1884, Pirie described having seen the collection of old estate papers and noted that the inventory totalled 68 documents at the time the estate changed hands again in 1733. Today only a few of the papers relevant to the old estate have survived, having been deposited in the Scottish Record Office by descendents of the family of Grant who purchased the lands (*Seafield Collection*). The details given by Fraser-Mackintosh were picked up by later authors who enlarged them into the full-blown legends which are still repeated today—in particular the lectures by Martin (1860, 1867, 1875) and descriptions by Bain (1882, 1911, 1922, 1928) have been quoted *ad nauseam*. On researching into what has been written on the subject, some 200 papers, articles and books relating to the Culbin Sands have been traced. These are of varying length and weight, and roughly half contain descriptions of the estate or mention aspects of its history: with the "facts" taken *verbatim* from these "authorities" and not uncommonly enchanced in the telling by having some additional embroidery tacked on.

Of all the authors who have written on the Culbin Sands, only one has urged caution in the acceptance of the popular version. The Rev. J.G. Murray (1938a) remarked "It might have been expected however that newspaper and magazine editors would exercise a measure of discretion before publishing in their columns fantastic legends which have been repeated *ad nauseam* during the last quarter of a century. Or do they imagine that their readers will swallow 'cauld Kail het again' if only it is served by a different writer every time". Fifty years later this is still fair comment and the same old story is still repeated: (c.f. Willis 1986, Harding 1986 and Lamb, 1991). Murray was an able local historian and in building his accounts of local family histories, obviously had access to private family documents no longer available for study.

In an attempt to separate fact from fiction, it was considered that a first course of action should be to check what Fraser-Mackintosh had actually said against any historical documents relating to the estate which could still be traced.

The very first "misquote" discovered was that the total area of the estate amounted to 3600 acres (1457ha.). Fraser-Mackintosh (1865a p.317) stated in a footnote, "It appears that for the satisfaction of one of the proprietors, a measurement of the sands has lately been made, and the area, on the authority of Wm. Sclanders, Esq., of Forres, is 3600 acres." So the 3600 acres was the area of the Culbin Sands ca. 1865 and not that of the Culbin estate in 1694.

Quoting from an "old deed", Fraser-Mackintosh describes the estate as: "All and hail the lands of Culbin, comprehending therein the lands, mill, fishings, and others under-written, viz.: All and hail that part of the lands and barony of Culbin called the Mains of Culbin, with the manor place, houses, biggings, yards, orchards, tofts, crofts, and hail pertinents of the same; the Hill of Findhorn, with houses, biggings, and pertinents, the ferme coble on the water of Findhorn, with liberties, commonties, and privileges thereof, with the mussell scalp and salmon fishing and pertinents, as well in fresh as salt waters of Findhorn, commonly called the Stells of Culbin with other fishings pertaining and belonging to the said lands and barony of Culbin, as well in fresh as salt waters; the lands of Mackrodder, alias Mirrietown: the lands of Aikenhead, alias Ranchkers, with houses, biggings, yards, orchards, doves, dovecots, tofts, crofts, parts, pendicles, outsets, fishings, as well in salt as fresh waters, annexis, connexis, dependencies, cottages, tenant's, tennandries, and service of free tenants and hail pertinents thereof, lying within the barony of Culbin and sheriffdom of Elgin and Forres: as also all and hail the remainder of the said lands and barony of Culbin: the lands of Binn, alias Middle Binn, with houses, biggings, yards, orchards, and pertinents of the same; all and hail the lands of Laick and Sandifield, the lands of Delaith, alias Delpottie, with the mill of Delpottie, multures and sequels of the said lands and barony of Culbin, with houses, biggings, yards, orchards, doves, dovecots, tofts, crofts, parts, pendicles, outsets, annexis, connexis, dependencies, tenant's, tenantries, and service of free tenants, and hail other pertinents of the same, lying within the barony of Culbin and Sheriffdom of Elgin and Forres afforesaid, together also with the teinds, both great and small, parsonage and vicarage of the hail barony, fishings, and others above written, with the pertinents; and sicklike all and hail the manse of the Chapel of Saint Ninian, with the yard, houses, biggings, crofts and pertinents of the same, lying within the parish of Dyke and sheriffdom of Elgin and Forres aforesaid; and, moreover, all and hail the salmon fishing on the water of Findhorn, called the common stell, alais the Sheriff Stells, with parts, pendicles, and universal pertinents of the same, used and wont, lying on the west side of the said water of Findhorn, within the parish of Dyke, regality of Kinloss, and sheriffdom of Elgin and Forres aforesaid; as also all and hail the lands of Earnhill, with the manor place, houses bigging, yards, orchards, parts and pendicles, and pertinents of the same, and all and hail the lands of Easter Binn with houses, biggings, yards, parts, pendicles, and pertinents of the same; both the said lands of Earnhill and Easter Binn, with the pertinents of the same, lying within the parish of Dyke and Moy, the sheriffdom of Elgin and Forres all united and incorporated into a hail and free barony, called the barony of Culbin, whereof the manor place is declared to be the principal messuage conform to a charter under the Great Seal granted by his late Majesty. All holden taxward of the Crown, excepting the said manse of the Chapel of St. Ninians, with the pertinents, which hold feu of the Crown, for the year feu-duty of ten shillings Scots money, and the said salmon fishing on the water of Findhorn, called the common stell or Sheriff Stell, with the pertinents, which hold feu of the Crown, for payment to the King or Lord of erection of the Abbey of Kinloss of the yearly feu-duty of five pounds ten shillings Scots money."

Many writers have fallen into the trap of quoting directly from this, and including "houses, biggings, yards, orchards, tofts, crofts, doves, dovecotes" etc. with each property as listed. This phraseology is that used in the conveyancing of the period by a "writer" who may not have seeen the property, and had to cover all eventualities in his list of an estate's assets, whether they existed or not. So, for example, there may never have been an orchard on the lands. The mains or home farm was by tradition the best farm on an estate, and on the best ground, usually close to the proprietor's residence. It could be run by a factor, or leased out to tenants or worked by the tenants of other farms on the estate as part of their ariage (bondage) (White, 1979). No mention is made in any of the charters or sasines as to the annual rents or size of the "Mains of Culbin" and it is probable that the term "Mains with its manor house" was also part of the conveyancing jargon of the period and that the laird stayed at the farm of Binn (of old called Middlebinn).

From Fraser Mackintosh's lists the properties controlled by the Culbin estate read:

> The Mains of Culbin
> The Lands of Binn, alias Middle Binn
> The Lands of Mackrodder, alias Mirrietown
> The Lands of Aikenhead, alias Ranchkers
> The Lands of Laik and Sandifield
> The Lands of Dolaith, alias Delpottie
> The Mill of Delpottie

The Lands of Earnhill
The Lands of Easter Binn
The Hill of Findhorn
The Mussel Scalp of the Hill of Findhorn
The Fishing Boat at the Hill of Findhorn
The Salmon Fishing of the Common or Sheriff's Stell
The Salmon Fishing of the Stell of Culbin
The Ferme Cobble on the Water of Findhorn
The Manse of the Chapel of St. Ninian

As other documents connected with the Kinnaird family were uncovered, in particular those contained in the Register of Sasines, it became apparent that there were differences between the various lists of the estate's holdings. Some were due to clerks of the period misinterpreting the handwriting in older documents when transcribing details for inclusion in later ones.

In Fraser-Mackintosh's "old deed" the lands of Aikenhead appear with the alias "Ranchkers". This appears as "Neuchkars" in Duff's 1694 case, but as Roughcarse in the 1682 sasines of his original wadset. (RS 29/2 p.411: RS 29/3 pp 116 & 127). Grazing rights of the Rough Carse are referred to in various sasines as having been settled in 1538. Bain (1911 p.223) states that the Rough Carse of Culbin is mentioned in a charter of the Knights Templar of St. John, as being the northern boundary of a block of land belonging to their order opposite Cothill and Maviston. Again The Hill of Findhorn and The Mussel Scalp of the Hill of Findhorn appear in some texts whereas the originals read "The Mussel Scalp thereof", i.e. The Mussel Scalp of the Hill of Findhorn. The "Ferme cobble" on the water of Findhorn should have read the "Ferrie cobble", while the "Manse and Chapel of St. Ninian" often appears instead of the "Manse of the Chapel of St. Ninian". Some mistakes may have arisen during the translation from the latin of old documents, as did "The salmon fishing and boat at the Hill of Findhorn" which in Latin started out as "The said fishing and white-fish boat at the Hill of Findhorn".

As each laird was aware that his power lay in preserving his property, he was careful to keep all his estate documents in his "charter chest". These could be passed to a writer for copying when any transactions involving the lands came up. It was found that long after a part of the Culbin estate had been sold off, the name of that property might reappear in a document listing the estate's holdings—wrongly entered by the person copying details from old charters—then this in turn might be re-copied.

An example of this is Easter Binn, which had once been part of the estate and is mentioned in 1453 as being part of the lands belonging to Gelis (Egidia) of Moravia of Culbin. This property had passed into the hands of a family of Dunbars at least as early as the start of the 17th century. In 1620 Walter Kinnaird, 2nd son of the Laird of Culbin, had a wadset on Easter Binn for the sum of 2500 merks, the owner redeemed the loan in 1625 (RS 28/3 p.18). Other documents show the lands remained in that family into the following century. It also appears that the small settlement at the Hill of Findhorn was part of the Easter Binn estate, and that its inhabitants crewed the white fish boats owned by the Laird (Murray 1921 and 1938b). No additional information on the ownership of the mussel scalps was uncovered. Without these the white fishing could not be undertaken, and they would be a great asset to their owner.

The lands of McRodder, alias Mirrietown, appears elsewhere as Muirtown, and again this figured in the 1453 document. It featured as part of Walter Kinnaird's lands at the time of his marriage in 1571 (Murray, 1938 p.12), and is entered on the 1590 ms. map by Timothy Pont as Moorton). Later, in *The Rental of the Bishoprick of Moray of 1641* it appears under the ownership of Ninian Dunbar of Grangehill (Fraser Mackintosh 1865b), and remained in the possession of that family into the following century (RS 29/5 p.244 and RS 29/6 p.35). Any connection with the Muirton Links mentioned by Bain (1911) could not be confirmed, but does seem probable.

There had been a family feud between the Kinnairds and the Falconers of Kincorth in 1610 (Murray 1938a p.13) and some 25 years after this Walter Kinnaird, possibly to make amends for the involvements of his father and grandfather in the affair, gave a hereditary sasine of the Manse of the Chapel of St. Ninian to Samuel Falconer of Kincorth and his son William, now minister of Dyke (RS 28/4 p.62). This remained in the hands of the Falconers until handed over to the Kirk Session of Dyke in 1673. The Laird of Culbin did, however, retain the superiority (Murray 1938a p.20). Only a small croft or parcel of ground went with the manse.

A summary of the above paragraphs is that the productive part of the Culbin estate has been effectively reduced to: Middle Binn, Laik and Sandifield, Delpottie with its mill and Earnhill, plus the salmon fishing and possibly the mussel scalps.

The most-quoted extract from Fraser-Mackintosh's account is the rental of the estate for the year 1693 which is produced in tabular form in Appendix 10. The document was included in the legal process before the Court of Session in 1694, which Baillie Duff of Inverness had brought against Alexander Kinnaird, the Laird of Culbin. This listed the rents of the estate as amounting to £2720 Scots, 640 Bolls of wheat, and similar quantities of bere, oats and oatmeal. The documents connected with the

Figure 23    The extent of the Barony of Culbin and the Old Findhorn Bar in 1680.

04

65

FINDHORN

nfold

64

Hill of Findhorn

63

62

carse

Cottar Town
of Tannachy

carse

Nether
Town
of Grange

61

Cottar Town
of Grange

Tannachy

Mill of
West Grange

Lingies
Town

60

Bogtown

Foord

FORRES

S.M.R.

04

court case are preserved in the West Register House, Edinburgh (CS29, box 164, 17 Feb. 1694) but a copy of this vital rental quoted by Fraser-Mackintosh as being included is not, in fact, there. Enquiry revealed that there was no need for this type of evidence to be preserved, and that it had most probably been returned to Duff after the hearing. This could have been the copy seen by Fraser-Mackintosh. A closer look at this rental shows that the list is not of 16 farms but of 16 tenants in 6 holdings, which are those listed in the previous paragraph. Of the three larger ones, Middle Binn supports 5 tenants, and Delpottie and Laik 4 each, while the remaining 3, Sandifield, Earnhill and Culbin have only one tenant each. This raises the question as to how much ground a single tenant could work, bearing in mind the traditional methods in use at the time (see p. 125).

## INFORMATION FROM DOCUMENTS FROM SLIGHTLY LATER PERIODS

Detailed annual rentals for Culbin and Kintessack for the years 1733 and 1734 are preserved among the Seafield Papers in the Scottish Record Office (GD 248/80 6), (Appendix 11). The 1733 rental for Culbin is quoted by Fraser-Mackintosh (1865a p.319) for comparison with the famous 1693 rental (Appendix 10) to illustrate the supposed drastic loss of revenue over the period. In the Kintessack rental the information listed against each tenant is extremely detailed and the acreage held by each man is recorded, together with the rents paid in grain, money and kind. The list showed a minimum of 23 tenants working one plough* of arable land. Grain rents at this period in Scotland are generally considered to have been one third of the harvested crop, while crop yields as low as only three times the amount sown were common (see White 1979, pp 73 *et. seq.* for discussion of yields). Taking an average sowing of one boll per acre, the yield can be calculated using the formula:

$$\text{Average Yield} = \frac{\text{Rent} \times 3}{\text{acreage} \times \text{bolls sown}}$$

which gives for Kintessack in 1733 a yield of 1.65 bolls per acre.

In 1706 a judicial estate rental was made up for the new laird of Grangehill after the death of his father. In this, Kintessack was stated to have 94 acres of arable land being worked by 20 tenants and with an

---

*A plough was an old land measure of 104 Scots acres = 131 English acres or 53ha. It was so called because it was the amount of land which could be ploughed in a year by a team of oxen. See Appendix 12.

expected rental of 157 bolls. This indicated a yield of 1.6 bolls per acre, a figure almost identical to that of 1733. In the 1733 rentals, the bere rents at Earnhill, Delpottie and Laik were 22, 32 and 32 bolls respectively. Assuming their yields to have been much the same as at Kintessack, these figures were divided by 1.65 to find the probable acreages. By this method Earnhill had 13.3 acres and Delpottie and Laik 19.4 acres each, making the total size of the three 52.1 acres.

A plan of the Estate of Moy dated 1776 can be studied in the Moray District Record Office, Forres (DGS P1). At this later date Earnhill and Delpottie were included in the lands of Moy and the plan shows the boundaries of these crofts and in addition full details of each field are given, including the acreage and outlines of the rigs (fig. 24, p.113). These figures add up Earnhill having 20 acres and Delpottie 22 approximately: a total of 42 acres. This was accompanied by 39 acres of pasture land. The size of these two holdings calculated from the 1733 rents was 32.7 acres, so there is only a modest degree of agreement here. There is no way of telling whether any boundary changes occurred in the intervening period, but a rental for the year 1772 (GD 158/5/4), which has little detail, shows the grain rents at Earnhill and Delpottie as remaining virtually unchanged at 23 bolls and 32 bolls respectively. Laik, meanwhile, which had a rental of 32 bolls in 1733, was reduced to 10 bolls, which may indicate a further encroachment of sand.

In 1682 Wm. Duff, baillie of Inverness, held a sasine (RS 29/3 p.116) on the Culbin estate and this included "The 5 ploughs land of Binn, commonlie or of old called Middlebin" with a yearly rental of 90 bolls of bere. This appears to be the only time the actual size of any of the properties on the estate has been given. If, in 1682, the crop yield was, say, 4 bolls per acre, then the grain rent would be 1.33 bolls per acre and a 90 boll rent would normally be expected from a 67.7 acre holding. This rent of 90 bolls is a very low figure indeed from what is termed a 5 Plough farm, and not that much more than the rents expected from the combined holdings of Earnhill, Delpottie and Laik. This hinges on the belief that the rent of 90 bolls was factual and not just the interest on the loan. Though these interpretations should be treated with caution, they do add to the suggestion that the popular beliefs as to the size of the old Culbin estate are in need of revision.

## THE IMPORTANCE OF THE FISHING RIGHTS HELD BY THE CULBIN ESTATE

From the Court of Session records of the 1760 fishing dispute, we learn that the fishing on the fresh water of the River Findhorn from the Sluy

Pool to the sea did belong in property to the Abbot and Convent of Kinloss from a charter from Robert III in 1394. 7/16 of the fishings were controlled by the Burgh of Forres, and the remaining 9/16 by private individuals. Parts of the latter were held on wadset by John Kinnaird, the uncle of the Laird of Culbin, for some four years from 1633, and soon after the wadset was redeemed, he purchased the farm of Hempriggs.

The salt water fishings of Findhorn Bay were described in the 1760 case as being divided into 3 stells on the west side of the bay and five on the east, "in terms of which a feu charter was granted by the Abbot and Convent (of Kinloss) to the Burgh (of Forres) on Dec. 22nd 1539 by which the right to fish on the west side of the river is ascertained to the Stell of Aithes Stell and 3/4 of Elvin Stell, the other 1/4 with the third west stell called the Common Stell having been before acquired by third parties." In 1631 Walter Kinnaird received from James Spens of Alves Kirktown a charter of the salmon fishing on the water of Findhorn called the common stell, alias the Sheriff's Stell on the west side of the river (RS 28/3 p.316). This was confirmed by Royal Charter in 1642 (Fraser-Mackintosh 1865a, p.315).

Walter's uncle John, mentioned above, had at some stage acquired part of the Aith Stell, his widow passing this on to their daughter Jean on her Marriage of Alexander Innes in 1655. There is no indication whether this fishing right had been purchased or inherited (Forbes 1864). Walter Kinnaird also controlled the East and West Stells of Culbin which were situated in the river channel of the Findhorn, after it flowed out of Findhorn Bay, to the north of Easter Binn (fig. 23, p.109). The Stells of Culbin were bounded on the east side by the Sheriff's Stell and on the west by the fishings owned by Hay of Lochloy. Details can be found in the sasines relating to the period when these fishings were on wadset to Dawsons of Findhorn 1667–1677. This stell was abandoned in 1701 when the river broke through the Old Bar and the channel filled with blown sand.

The sasine of 1682 held by Baillie Duff of Inverness (RS 29/3 p.6) shows the combined rents from the Sheriff's Stell and Culbin Stells amounted to 30 barrels good and sufficient clean well salted salmon. No figures were available for the price of salmon towards the end of the 17th century, but taking into account prices before and after the period in question, an average of £25 Scots per barrel would produce an annual income of £750 Scots from these stells.

## TOTAL ANNUAL RENTS AND VALUE OF THE PROPERTY

If we assume that the grain rents from Culbin estate were made up of 90 bolls from Middlebin, and (using the 1733 rents) 83 1/2 bolls from Earnhill,

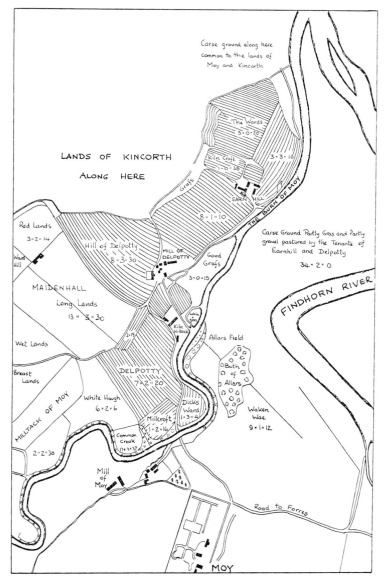

Figure 24    Earnhill and Delpottie when part of Moy in 1776.

Delpottie plus the mill, and Laik, after the deduction of the minister's stipend, the total would come to 173 1/2 bolls. With the price of bere at 5 merks per boll, as in 1679 (Rampini 1897) this would bring in an annual revenue of £578 Scots. This figure would rise with the rising price of bere in the famine years of the 1690s, and at £5 per boll would fetch £867 Scots. (The price of bere was stablised by law at £12 per boll in 1699 after 7 years bad harvest—Dunbar Dunbar 1865 p.31). So as a first approximation, the fishings held by the estate were of equal importance to the agriculture, and a total annual income of somewhere between £1328 and £1617 could be expected.

As far as the value of land in this period is concerned, it was commonly put at around 20 times the annual rent. Reduced values for deteriorating circumstances might be described as "Only worth a 10-year rent or purchase. In fact, Fraser-Mackintosh (1865a), using the 1733 rents for Earnhill, Delpottie and Laik calculated "a 22-year purchase" for these lands with the price of bere at £5 Scots per boll, and this he found to be £10,872:15s:4d. With the price of bere at 5 merks per boll this would have been reduced to £7810. It is of interest to note that in 1733 John Duff, the then owner, went bankrupt and the properties had been sold for £11,366:19s:8d Scots.

Wadsets were always biased in favour of the person giving the loan, and we have in 1673 a sasine showing Earnhill and Delpottie with its mill, being held on wadset by Wm. Dunbar of Kintessack against 8500 merks (£5667 Scots) and in 1682, one showing the whole estate including the fishings being held in wadset by Wm. Duff against 25,000 merks (£16,667 Scots). In the latter case if we take the annual rents of Culbin to amount to £1328, the wadset was for 12.5 times this amount, and if the higher figure of £1617 is used, then 10.3 times. At the final sale, the estate fetched £20259:10s:6d. A 20-year purchase at £1328 per annum would put the value of the estate at £26,560 and this would fall in line with the statement made in the final disposition in 1698, that the purchase price was less by fully £6000 Scots than the amount of debts due to Wm. Duff and Sir James Abercrombie of Birkenbog, the only other preferential creditor (Murray 1938a p.40).

Taking into account the accepted crop yields and rent structures throughout Scotland in the period, and bearing in mind the primitive state of agriculture in the north in these pre-improvement days, the 1693 rental looks ridiculously high if we are to agree that the Culbin estate was of a much smaller size than the popular accounts would have us to believe. There then enters the possibility that the rental was an attempt at some form of evaluation of the estate, albeit incomplete.

On comparing the 1693 list of tenants and holdings with the 1733 rental (Appendices 10 and 11) it could be concluded that the former was one of the major tenants only, there being 5 in Middlebin, 4 each in Laik and Delpottie and 1 in Earnhill. Using the same annual grain rent of 173 1/2 bolls, then a total of 2560 bolls would equal a 14 year income and then £2720 Scots money rent divided by 14 would produce a figure of £194 per annum. Though this is speculation, it at least produces a factor by which realistic figures have to be multiplied to equal the popular ones.

# THE BOUNDARIES OF THE OLD CULBIN ESTATE

The only record of the actual size of any of the Culbin properties is found in the 1682 sasines held by Wm. Duff on the estate. These give the size of Middle Binn as being 5 ploughs (265ha.) but nowhere is there any mention of estate boundaries and there are no detailed maps dating from the period.

It was considered that if a map was constructed of the neighbouring properties using data from the following century, then their boundaries would give an indication of the outline of the east side of the old Culbin estate and possibly allow a 5-plough Middle Binn to be fitted between there and the shingle ridges with some degree of confidence.

The original size of Easter Binn is also known, having been given in a sasine of 1625 as 2 ploughs (106ha.). From the 1667 Valued Rent of the Shire of Moray (Shaw 1827), Culbin was rated at £913:18s:4d, Easter Binn at £390:17s:2d, and Kincorth at £371:18s:6d, giving an approximate ratio of 5 : 2 : 2. From this it would seem fair to say that Kincorth was also about 2 ploughs in extent.

Peter May's map of 1758 which accompanied the fishing case of 1760, contains much detail of the field system and holdings beside the River Findhorn, including the outlines of Binsness (formerly Easter Binn), (fig. 25, p.117). When this map is reduced to the scale of 1 : 25,000 and compared with the modern O.S. sheet NH 96/NJ 06, Binsness on May's map is found to cover an area of 52.6ha. (including 3.7ha. for the Hill of Findhorn). This is as near as matters 1 plough, or half the original size of Easter Binn. An additional "plough" is now inserted on the map to the north of the 1758 Binsness boundary, using as the northern margin the edge of the shingle ridges (fig. 22, p.103) and this together with the mapped lands of Binsness now represents the original Easter Binn.

Some field systems are shown by May round Laik, Kincorth and upstream past Delpottie, but if the greater detail from the 1776 plan of Moy estates is used (fig. 24, p.113) the 21ha. occupied by Delpottie and its mill and Earnhill can be transferred to the working sheet in more detail, as can the courses of the River Findhorn and the Moy Burn. The 1758 map also shows the borders of the carse lands along the river and these can also be transferred. This is important in that they cover a considerable area, and being liable to flooding at the times of the "high stream tides", were only used for grazing and not included in the size of the farm lands.

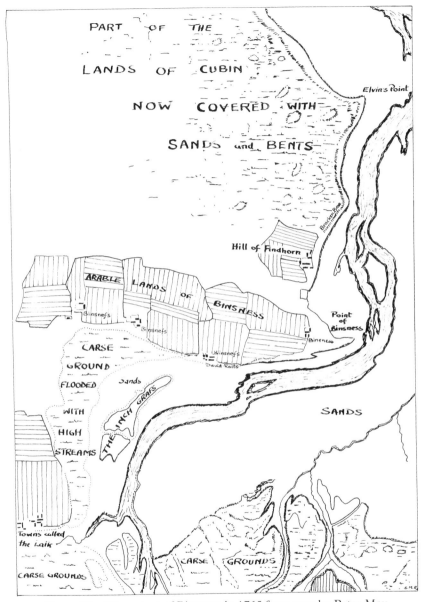

Figure 25    The extent of Binsness in 1765 from map by Peter May.

In 1776 the fields of Delpottie and Earnhill were flanked on the northwest side by the Belmack Burn and this also formed the northern boundary of Kintessack. The line of the burn, stretching back to the Clay Moss (fig. 23, p.109) is now used as the boundary between Kintessack and Kincorth. The northwest boundary of Kincorth against Culbin is taken as being the same as today—a line from near Wellhill to Laik. The area of Kincorth thus enclosed covers some 113ha. of arable land. In view of the wet nature of the ground along the southern side, this may well have been smaller in the old days, but the whole does approximate to the "2-plough" size.

Next, using Peter May's field system to the north side of The town called the Laik, a small 11ha. block can be inserted to represent Laik. Whether or not to allocate some area for Sandifield is a problem. It does not figure in the 1733 rental, but is always mentioned in conjuntion with Laik in Culbin documents up to the time of the final sale. At this stage there is a 10ha. block left on the working map, beween Laik and Easter Binn, and as Sandifield showed one tenant in the 1693 rental, against Laik's four, 3ha. could be allocated to it from this block. When these conjectural boundaries are drawn in, the remaining arable lands enclosed between them and the shingle ridges amount to 207ha.

There is no mention in any of the records of there ever having been a Wester Binn, and with the distinct probability that the "Mains of Culbin" was a conveyancing term, it would seem fair to allocate the remaining 207ha. of arable ground to Middle Binn, which was 5 ploughs (265ha.) in extent. This leaves 58ha., or slightly more than 1 plough to be found. By this approach, the eastern margin of Middle Binn has now been more or less fixed, so any adjustments have to be made on the other margins.

Where the shingle has been seen, it is mapped on fig. 22 (see p.103) with full lines, and its probable maximum extent is marked by dashed lines. It is not known how far the Middle Binn, or for that matter Easter Binn boundaries extended into the rougher land, but a 100m wide strip along this margin would accommodate the remaining 58ha. Again, as this is only a calculation, the extra lands may have been situated in one or two small blocks, and either way could possibly affect the boundary of Easter Binn. However it seems certain that the 58ha. was not on arable land.

The complete picture is shown in fig. 23 (see p.109) and satisfies the evidence on the ground and agrees with what documentary evidence has survived. It reduces the 16 farms to 5 and the 3600 acres to 735 (1457ha. to 298ha.).

# THE VILLAGE OF FINDHORN

The village of Findhorn is closely linked in legend to the Barony of Culbin, with both places having been overwhelmed by natural disasters. There are varying accounts in the local literature as to where the village was situated and how and when it was destroyed—the differences generally arising from later and more popular authors having misinterpreted or ignored the earlier records, and weaving a more dramatic tale.

Timothy Pont's map of 1590 (fig. 3, p.9) shows the village situated on the bar near the mouth of Findhorn Bay, but with no detail. Blaeu's Moravia of 1654, (Appendix 2) being based on Pont's work, has no different information, but in Grenville-Collin's survey of 1685 we see the tiny village clearly situated on the bar rather than being at the head of Findhorn Bay. Maps later than 1701 show the village in its new position after the breaching of the bar (Avery 1730, Roy 1755 and May 1758 & 1765). May's maps have the former river channel marked and also the old position of the village.

The coastal erosion processes and problems were exactly the same in these far-off days as they are today, with a constant movement of materials westwards along the beaches (see p.29). The sand and shingle that formed the Old Bar had been eroded out of Burghead Bay and as the bay enlarged into a half-moon, some degree of shelter to the beaches developed with the result that the supply of materials moving westwards from that source decreased, and the waves began eroding the seaward side of the bar itself. Among the spates and storms which affected the area during the 17th century, Brodie (1863) records that on December 19th, 1653 there occurred the largest tide and overflowing of the sea for 40 years, when some houses at Findhorn had been taken away. Martin (1860, 1867) pointed out that the natives of Findhorn were aware of the potential threat to their village from the river on one side and the sea on the other, and as erosion progressed, they read the signs and began building a new village some 1.6km to the southeast, where the present village now stands. As a result, when the bar was finally breached, there was no loss of life.

There is no agreement on the date the river broke through the Old Bar and destroyed the first village. In the Court of Session Fishing Dispute (1760) it was recorded as "as ... and appears by a Number of Declarations produced in the process, that the old Town of Findhorn was destroyed in the year 1704". This was repeated by Shaw (1775): Grant and Leslie

119

(1798) gave 1701 as the date: Young (1871) suggested 1702, while Ritchie (1932) gave Sunday morning, 11th October, 1702, which was the date used by Steers (1937). Bain, in customary style, describing the blinding and bewildering sandstorm overwhelming the Culbin estate, went on to say: "And to add to the horrors of the scene, the sand had choked the mouth of the river Findhorn, which now poured its flooded waters amongst the fields and homesteads, accumlating in lakes and pools till it rose to a height by which it was able to burst the barrier to the north, and find a new outlet to the sea, in its course sweeping to destruction the old village of Findhorn". This would push the date as far back as 1694.

Writing in the *First Statistical Account* for 1791–1799, the Rev. John Dunbar of Dyke described how the old channel of the river was still visible and that the Old Bar was by then cut off by the highest tides, save at one point near its western end. Stones from the old houses could be seen lying at the bottom of the channel at the mouth of the bay, more than half a mile west of the present village and marked the original site. He added that people who had been alive 40 years earlier had remembered seeing stones being moved to the east side of the river and used in building the first houses of the new village. This ties in with the statements given in the 1760 lawsuit, but may be a direct quote from it. With a new bar growing west across its mouth, the river was again unable to keep a direct channel open into deep water. The Old Bar he described as being then covered with sand and bent-grass and only used for sheep pasture and temporary huts for salmon fishermen. He then stated that the old town stood 3/4 mile west of the present village.

Grant and Leslie (1798) gave the position of the old village as "a mile northwest from its present position and now at the bottom of the sea." These statements led to some confusion in later years. Standing in Findhorn today and looking west or northwest, the old site of the village would appear, on this information, to have lain roughly on the northeast corner of the Culbin on the other side of the river mouth. In spite of the fact that Peter May's maps (fig. 4, p.11) showed the position of the first village, and the evidence in the 1760 lawsuit, the Rev. William Robertson writing of the Parish of Kinloss in the *Second Statistical Account* of 1842, believed that the first village stood on the bar, that a second was then built on the west bank of the river opposite, and when it in turn was destroyed, the present one replaced it. This started the legend of the three villages, which still persists.

Martin (1867) described Findhorn at the time of the overwhelming of the Culbin estate, as a bustling port with wharves lined with warehouses and thronged by seamen. A few records remain from this period of shipments from Findhorn of cargoes of barley, malt, salmon and white fish to various east coast ports of Scotland and England and also to Norway, the Low Countries, France and Portugal (Dunbar Dunbar 1865). After repeating the three villages story, Bain (1911) stated "For nearly a century before that date (the breaching) the Port of Findhorn had been the centre of a large shipping and mercantile trade, principally with the continent, but particularly with Rotterdam and Bordeaux". Repeating Dunbar Dunbar's lists of exports and imports he added "Long rows of warehouses and cellars for stocking the precious cargoes ran along the quay and crowds of sailors and labourers frequented its pier. Many of the northern Lairds engaged in the trade; some of them made fortunes by it; others were ruined, these latter not having discernment to leave off the speculations when the tide turned".

From the names given on the comparatively few bills of lading quoted, it could be concluded that only the most opulent of the lairds indulged in this trade, aided by their merchant toadies. Tayler and Tayler (1914) suggested that Baillie William Duff of Inverness, his nephew William Duff of Dipple and Sir James Calder of Muirtown controlled virtually all the foreign trade north of Aberdeen. Their exports came cheaply, being mostly the rents of their tenants, while the imports listed were luxuries none of which would be aimed at the common people, who, when they went to pay their rents, found that the price of barley had somehow been lowered— "the poor-man's boll".

Scottish trade was carried on mainly in ships built in the Netherlands or sometimes in Norway, but owned by Scotsmen. Vessels operating from Scottish ports had to be small and rarely exceeded 100 tons because Scotland had no rivers which were navigable but non-tidal, and most harbours dried out at ebb tide (Duncan 1975). There was no engineering capacity to build long quays, so ships came into harbours like the Findhorn channel at high tide and anchored. As the tide fell, they grounded and unloaded their cargo over the side on to the sand. As the pier at Findhorn was not built until 1778, it must be logical to dismiss Martin's (and Bain's) description of the bustling port as embroidery—something that urges caution on how much weight to put on their other descriptions. As there were no piers, wharves, warehouses or cellars destroyed when the old village was swept away, attention should be focused on the shortage of sheltered harbours along the Moray coast and not on the small community at this river mouth.

The size of the Merchant Fleet ca. 1680 is very much in doubt. Of the coasting trade we have very little knowledge with sketchy Customs records being the main, if not the sole source of information (Duncan 1975). In Crammond (1903) we find that records of custom dues on exports of wool, hides and skins from "the ports of Elgin" go back as far as 1365. Most early shipments of corn and salmon from Findhorn went to Leith and exports of salmon to the Netherlands in 1492–1503 were probably transhipped at Aberdeen. Shipments of cod were included in exports in 1504.

To put things more into perspective, Hume-Brown (1891) has in his *Early Travels* a visit to Inverness and Murray in 1655 by Thomas Tucker, who prepared a report for Oliver Cromwell on Scottish Ports. Tucker made the following comments on trade of the period. "The trade in the port of Inverness is only a coast trade, there being no more than a single merchant in all the towne, who brings home sometime a little timber, salt or wine. Here is a collector, a cheque and one wayter who attends here and looks (as the occasion serves) to Garmouth and Findhorne in Murrayland, two small places whence some 60 lasts of salmon a year are sent out, for which salt is brought in from France and sometimes a small vessel comes in from Holland or Norway."

Towards the end of the century, but more particularly into the beginning of the following one there was a considerable increase in trade from the Moray Firth area judging from the dates on the bills that have survived. Mackay (1915), commenting on Tucker's finding only one merchant in Inverness in 1655, described how in the time of John Stewart, a merchant in Inverness who traded between 1715 and 1752, this number had increased to 20, and that Stewart owned some 12 ships, skippered by men of his own family.

In spite of the probable very small extent of the foreign trade from Findhorn in this early period, it has been widely quoted as an unparalleled example of the enterprising nature of the Lairds in Moray in establishing these early links with the continent. That they did keep an ear to the ground is shown by, when in 1685, there was a disasterous harvest in Scandanavia and in Scotland a good one, there were substantial shipments of grain from North East Scotland to Norway.

# AGRICULTURE AND FARM LIFE IN 17th CENTURY MORAY

The grain rents of the Culbin estate for the year 1693 as listed by Fraser-Mackintosh (1865a) were not only the largest in Moray but also in Scotland at that period. In fact, they are so large as to arouse suspicion when it is realized that, in the period in question, the improvements in agricultural methods, which were well established in lowland Scotland, did not reach Moray until some 70 years after the Culbin estate had been abandoned. The uniformity of rents, indicating equal distribution of the land between tenants, was also unknown elsewhere.

In order to get a balanced view of what was possible in the farming world of these far-off days, and what was not, it will be prudent to have a closer look at the agriculture of the period.

Reviews of agricultural life and methods in the latter half of the 17th century as seen through the eyes of authors who lived from 100 to 300 years later, are found in: Donaldson (1794), Grant and Leslie (1798), Leslie (1811), Graham (1901), Symon (1959), Fenton (1976) and White (1979). From these sources the following summary has been compiled.

The mains farm, usually close to the Laird's house and situated on the best land, could be let out to tenants or looked after by a factor. The tenants in turn paid rent for their lands and this was usually paid in grain with perhaps a small sum of money. Additional rent in kind was also included in the total, and this included meal, poultry, eggs, butter, yarn, fodder etc. One charge in the rentals which is of great interest is that of one hen per fire in the farmtouns. These "reek-hens" provide a measure of the number of households in the community, where few, if any, other records exist. For example, the 1733 rentals show 38 households in Kintessack, 8 in Laik and 20 in Delpottie (Appendix 11).

The most resented part of a tenant's rent was the time spent in providing a certain number of days' work on the Laird's home farm, usually in ploughing and at harvest time. This work took priority over work on the tenant's own holding. Each tenant had to cut, dry and deliver a stated number of loads of peats to the Laird each summer, and in winter, after threshing the corn, deliver their own grain rent to the laird's storehouse or to a specified market. The estate's mill was also maintained by the tenants as part of their dues and they were bound to have their own grain

123

ground there. With all these additional tasks imposed on him, the tenant had little time to concentrate on his own holding, while the laird, having all the necessities of life delivered to his door, was loathe to change the system which stood as a barrier to progress.

The pattern of agriculture in vogue in the final days of the Culbin estate was one which had been established for a long time. Several tenants worked together in the joint cultivation of each farm, and the pattern of settlement which this produced was the grouping of the farmsteads and houses of the tenants into a cluster known as a ferme toune. While the estate was the basic unit of decision making and the focus of the community, the parish church yielded increasing power in local administration.

The occupants of the tounes, because of their limited resources, had to work together, pooling their labour and equipment. This communal working resulted in the distribution of the farm work being organised from the equality point of view rather than efficiency, and was geared towards subsistence rather than production for the market. However it had long been encouraged by the lairds as a means of providing a basic living from the land for as many people as possible. The power of the laird lay, not in the money raised from the land, but in the number of fighting men he could raise. Changes to more up-to-date methods had already taken place in Lowland Scotland, but the old ways were to persist in the Highlands until well into the following century, and when the changes did finally arrive, they were more disruptive due to the delay.

The tenants were the backbone of rural society but there could be a large gap between the more prosperous and the less able. With the pooling of equipment and labour, 4, 6 or even 8 tenants might be involved in the working of one farm. Apart from the laird and his family, the tenants were the only persons named in estate documents, because they paid the rents. People below the level of tenants and who made up the bulk of the rural population, seldom had any share of the land, perhaps not even the right to graze a cow, and were of no interest to the lairds. There was therefore little detail recorded of life at this level. The tenant hired and fired his own cottars and labourers and when he moved, they moved as well, but this was not often.

The cottars were essentially unpaid labourers who worked for the tenant on his holding and were granted a small portion of arable land and some grazing, usually with a cot house and a kale yard. Some were craftsmen of a kind, weavers, tailors, shoemakers etc., and supplemented their meagre incomes by catering for the needs of the small community. A few more skilled labourers might sometimes be employed directly by the estate on a daily or piece-work basis. Farm servants were usually hired for a year at a time, and got a cot house, a kale yard and pasture for 2–3 cows and an allowance of meal. Unmarried farm workers lived in and there were, at the lowest level, some servants, perhaps widows, who got accommodation and some sustenance in return for such tasks as herding cattle. The kirk session kept an eye on the hiring of servants in case unknown vagrants might get absorbed into the parish.

The arable land was divided into infield and outfield, where the infield lay close to the house and received all the availabe manure from the dung heap. It was in cultivation year after year without rest, much like a garden. In rotation, one third might be manured and planted in barley, and the remaining two thirds in oats without manure. The ratio of infield to outfield was usually 1 : 2, but could be reversed in fertile tracts. Cattle, horses and sheep were kept on common pasture in summer, sometimes being taken into the hill country to the south. Some might periodically be enclosed in parts of the outfield, thus providing extra manure there, and this part might later be planted in oats. However, once the harvest was over, the whole land became open pasture for the township and was rapidly trampled into mud. Over the winter, once the grass had been used up, there was only the straw thrashed from the crops, and the animals that survived were in a very sorry state, and were often too emaciated to be yoked to the plough. Sometimes they had to be carried out to the pasture— a process known as "the lifting".

Ploughing was a very primitive process, with the plough itself being made almost entirely of wood and having a crudely-shaped mould board which made it very unwieldy. It was drawn by a team of eight oxen, and sometimes by as many as twelve, with perhaps four tenants pooling resources and sharing the labour. While a strong man held the plough, a second led the team, walking backwards to stop the oxen when the plough hit stones. Another went in front with a spade to fill up hollows and a fourth goaded lagging beasts. This "cortege" could scratch only a very small area in a day, and that poorly. The old Scots landmeasures (Appendix 12) show the units such as the plough, defined as the acreage that one team of oxen could plough in a season.

The land was ploughed in the pattern of ridge and furrow, which was standard almost everywhere, regardless of the site, with adjacent ridges being allocated to different tenants to provide fair shares. The method furnished the only method of drainage at that time and the ridges were the basic working units for the pre-improvement farming, with the width in particular adapted to the hand-sowing of grain and to shearing it with a sickle. Always being ploughed up towards the centre, some rigs reached up to 0.9m in height on the crowns, and became fixtures, often appearing on estate plans (cf. Peter May's map of 1765 and Plan of Moy 1776). The old rigs varied from 5.5m to 11m or more in width and often took a curved form due to the distance needed to swing a team of oxen. The rigs which were discovered in the Culbin are 12.0m wide on average, but here the soil is very thin, measuring only 30cm in the centres of the rigs. The soil rests with a horizontal base on white sand and it is of interest to note that this lower surface has seldom been disturbed by the plough.

After sowing the crop, almost all the summer was taken up in cutting, drying and carting peats and turf for fuel for their own use and for the laird, but most important was the collecting of earth, turf, sand and clay for mixing into the dungheap. Old thatch and turf walls and roofs of the houses were periodically scrapped and thrown into the midden to help to create compost and additional manure was obtained by flooring the sheep-pens with turf and later clearing it out. The cutting of turf and thatch for the maintainance of the houses was also done in this period and took up a large portion of the time.

Crop yields were very poor at this time, and the traditional expression "Ane to saw, ane to gnaw and ane to pay the laird with" is founded on hard facts. Direct reference to crop yields of the period suggests that in fertile parts 4 : 1 was considered a fair average return. These modest yields were not improved until liming, ridging and burning, and less exhausting rotations were undertaken. The application of seaweed was known to markedly improve the yield of barley, but the boundaries of the Culbin estate lay against the river channel and not the sea beach proper, where any seaweed would be claimed by Muirtown estate. Rentals were based traditionally on one third of the normal annual product. A little flax and hemp might be grown, but while mention is made of kale yards and of kale being an essential part of the diet in order to keep scurvy at bay, Leslie (Grant & Leslie 1798) goes as far as to say "Gardens of every kind were wholly unknown among the common people. They only cultivated barley and oats: bread and water were their chief subsistence and meal and milk their highest luxury." Donaldson (1794, p.25) described the average country diet of this later period, and though still very restricted, it seems luxurious when compared to the above.

Farm implements were all home made, and like the plough described above, were rudimentary. Harrows were all of wood, including the teeth, which were positioned at random, as the problem of the best arrangement had not yet been solved. Grain and meal were transported in sacks slung over the horses' backs. Wicker panniers hung on either side of the horses were used for carrying dung and sheaves of corn. As soon as wheels became available, the kellach was used. This consisted of a conical basket suspended in a square frame with a crude wooden axle and wheels at one end and shafts projecting from the other. It never went beyond the farm boundaries, the panniers remained for that. Light carts appeared for carrying peats and turf, but were skeletal arrangements of thin bars. Ropes, backbands and traces were twisted out of pliant rushes and horsehair while collars and saddles were made of straw.

## YEARS OF REPORTED DEARTH AND FAMINE IN EAST SCOTLAND, 1550 - 1700

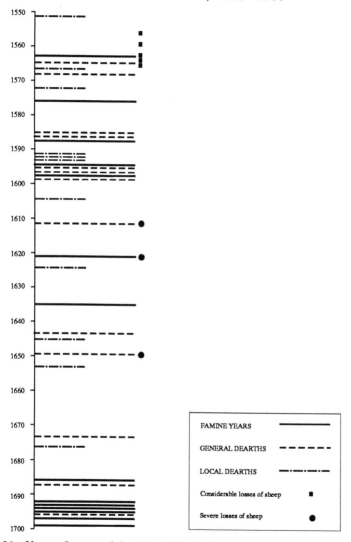

Figure 26    Years of reported dearth and famine in East Scotland 1550–1700 (from Lamb, 1982).

Societies where agriculture is at a subsistence level are always vulnerable from climatic disasters, and judging from the frequency of periods with abnormally high grain prices, there had been many severe shortages both locally and nationally from 1500 onwards. With ploughing slow and drainage, at its best, rudimentary, both sowing and harvesting tended to be late, increasing the chances of crop failure. Long winters resulted in heavy animal mortality and this in turn affected the amount of land that could then be ploughed. The whole 150 years had been a period of climatic deterioration, and in spite of the prominance given to the famine period with seven successive years of crop failures in the 1690s, other periods may have been equally as bad, especially around 1623 (see Lamb 1982 for a detailed review of the climate of this period and fig. 26, p.127).

These were the days of the plantation of Northern Ireland, the establishment of mercenary armies made up almost entirely of Scots, which served both in England and on the continent, and the disasterous Darien Scheme. Every adult in Scotland would have had personal experience of a major period of shortage, and family tragedy at some time in his life. During a famine the first to be affected and most dramatically, were the itinerant poor and then the day-labourers, workers and cottars who depended on money wages and who had to buy grain rather than grow it. In the 1690s as many as 200,000 people in Scotland were begging from door to door. There are accounts of men trekking over the mountains to buy grain in Moray and harrowing tales of the poor starving to death in the streets of Elgin. It is estimated that up to a fifth of the total population of Scotland died in this period. The more able-bodied, including discharged soldiers, formed dangerous bands variously called Sorners or Egyptians and were severely legislated against. Cattle rustling by Highlanders from the west was commonplace.

Looking out over a dreary landscape, which was in general bare and treeless, with only ill-made tracks for roads, and seeing impoverished natives living in dark, mean and smoky hovels, it is no wonder that travellers from the more fortunate south considered the national characteristics of the Scots to be sloth, ignorance and poverty.

Against this backdrop, how can we be convinced of the "highly cultivated fields, waving with heavy corn, the rich meadows dotted here and there with thriving herds and the extensive pastures with numerous flocks"?

# BUILDINGS ON THE OLD CULBIN ESTATE

The general improvements in agriculture which eventually reached Moray around 1760 were quickly followed by the building by the landowners of magnificent mansion houses in landscaped grounds with large enclosed gardens. Prior to this period the proprietors' dwellings were of a simpler form but still vastly superior to the hovels which housed their tenants.

Standing on a sand-dune "upwards of 100 feet in height" and which the local people believed covered the mansion house of Culbin, Martin (1869) recalled the time when "it stood fair and beautiful, and in apparent security, embowered amidst rows of tall shady trees, with its beautiful garden, its fruitful orchard and its spacious lawn..." He then described how, some eighty years earlier, after several days of furious sand drifting "a great part of the old mansion appeared, standing as a skeleton, apart from the great mass of sand in which it had been entombed. It was firmly and substantially built, and contained a number of finely dressed stones. While it lay exposed, it was used by the people of the neighbourhood as a quarry, and many a fair building in the district now posseses some of the good substantial stones that once graced the old baronial mansion of Culbin." Soon another sand-blow covered it up but later one of the chimney tops was seen "peering like a hugh march-stone above the sand, only to vanish again with the next storm". About 1920, sandstone blocks bearing parts of the family coat of arms were found, and during the 1930s a complete outline of foundation stones was exposed a short distance to the northwest of Kincorth. Anderson (1938) described them: "There is little doubt as to their being the foundations of the mansion house, the proximity of large kitchen middens and a circular mound, which is probably the doocot, plus the size of the house all pointing to this". Unfortunately he gave no exact locality or measurements.

As to Martin's description of the house and policies—using the style of Sir T. Dick Lauder, he dramatized his tales by the inclusion of additional "facts" and succeeded in giving a very good description of a post-improvement style of manor, rather than of one from the earlier period. Avenues of trees would have been out of place in the treeless Lower Moray, and the beautiful garden, fruitful orchard and spacious lawn more in line with the author's prose than the reality of impoverished lands during a prolonged period of famine.

During the 17th century there was already shortage of wood in lowland Moray and taking into consideration the lack of transport, houses had to be constructed from the materials most readily available. For instance, in the district near the mouth of the Spey, house walls were made entirely of rounded river boulders embedded in layers of clay and straw—a method known as "clay and boule". Inland, where more regular shaped building stone was available, the walls might be made of alternate layers of stone and turf (Fenton 1968). Between the Findhorn and the Nairn, where there was no stone available, the walls of the dwellings of the tenants and cottars were made entirely of turf or "feal" as it was called locally (Grant & Leslie, 1798). Such walls would be no more than 1.7m in height, and approximately 0.9m wide at the base narrowing to 0.45m at the top. These walls could not carry the weight of the roof and this was supported by means of stout timber cruck frames which stood on the ground (fig. 27, p.131). Cross-members on these supported a framework of thin, split branches on which was laid a thick covering of turf. The roof was thatched with broom or marram grass held on by weighted straw ropes and pegs or by nets of the same material (Walton 1957).

The cruck frames could have been of varied types, but due to the shortage of timber they remained the property of the laird when the tenants moved. The crucks were placed at an almost standard distance apart (2.75m) and this was an accepted unit of measurement: houses being referred to as "2-coupled" or '3-coupled" etc. Any increase in size of a house was made by the addition of extra couples. Width too was a fairly standard unit and was probably that found by trial and error to be the most efficient—3.65m.

The inside of the house was divided by a central wall, opposite which was the door, traditionally in the middle of the house. The building was thus divided into two, with the family living in one end and in the other a cow or cows tethered to an upright post in the centre, with a hay-store beyond. Other animals and chickens also lived indoors. The midden stood outside the door.

As dry turf is very flammable, a fireplace in the centre of the floor was necessary, round which the family slept, with perhaps a baffle to deflect the draught from the door. Furniture was minimal and rudimentary. The floor was of clay plastered in a thick layer over flat beach pebbles. The interior walls might also have been plastered with clay. There were no windows—perhaps a hole stuffed with old clothes at night while the door was often no more than a hurdle.

The walls, but more particularly the roof, had to be replaced at approximately 2-yearly intervals. The old sods and the thatch were thrown

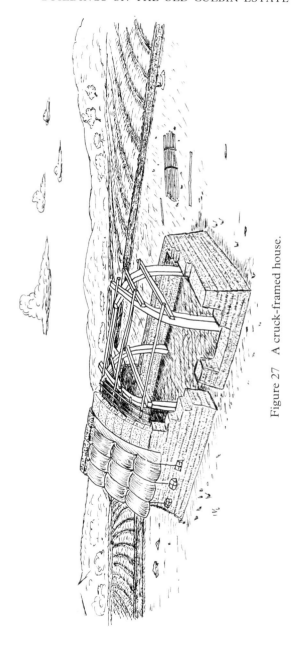

Figure 27 A cruck-framed house.

on to the midden to be mixed with the dung to make better compost. The practice of using turf or "feal" as the primary material for walls and houses in the Highlands is well documented by accounts by travellers from the early 16th to the 18th centuries and in the *Second Statistical Account* there are reports of turf houses in Moray being used as late as the 1840s.

A most interesting account by Noble (1984) described in detail the experimental building of such a turf house at the Highland Folk Museum in Kingussie and the many unexpected problems that were encountered. His comments on turf-cutting are worthy of note:

"Turf-cutting was a long, tedious procedure, and to supply the needs of this one building—not particularly large—absorbed in excess of twelve hundred man-hours. Even assuming that in a traditional township the pool of labour was a dozen or more able-bodied males, this is still a considerable investment of community time per building. The area of turf required was even more startling. Almost exactly an acre of ground was flayed to produce the walling material, with another two hundred square yards of divot being used on the roof. It is little surprising, therefore, that the landowners and the government were always fulminating and passing acts of parliament "anent the cutting of turf". A township of twenty buildings must have devastated the surrounding pasture. (And that takes no account of feal dykes). In 1763 we find the Laird of Grant complaining that the tenants were taking 3 to 4 weeks in the year repairing their houses, which time might be much better employed in ploughing the land or making dunghills.

The turf houses of the tenants and their labourers were grouped into small cottar-tounes, usually situated on poorer marginal land. The hovels that housed the poorer labourers were very small, only some 3 m square and could be built in a day. There is a record of the remnants of a house being exposed in the Culbin Sands about 1830 (Martin 1869). The walls were described as being "formed entirely of a firm clay turf which had been carefully cut and regularly placed. A few wooden supports, very much decayed, were still remaining. The floor was neatly causewayed with rounded stones from the beach and above this was a layer of clay about four inches in thickness." Mathewson (1878) recorded finding numbers of brass buckles round about the ruins of one of the houses which was uncovered from the sand, but unfortunately gave no other details.

In the dry environment of the Culbin abandoned turf dwellings would simply crumble to dust when exposed to the elements. It is therefore not so surprising that so little of the "Buried Barony" ever "reappeared".

# THE MURRAYS OF CULBIN

King David I (1124–1153) had spent much of his early life in England and had been influenced by the Anglo-Norman court there. Following the lead given by his elder brothers Edgar and Alexander I, he transformed the kingdom of Scotland into a feudal state by delegating royal authority, power, lands and wealth. The whole process of consolidation lasted almost exactly 200 years, from the beginning of the reign of Edgar ca. 1094 to 1296 when the war with England broke out.

Men of Norman and Flemish stock were encouraged to settle in Scotland and many of these were merchants and craftsmen but some were clearly designed from the beginning to be *domini* or lords in the new country. In this way Scotland became a land of opportunity and many of today's well known leading families were founded in this period. The lordships then granted were the principal means of increasing the royal authority. The chief tenants were obliged to put in regular attendance at court and a standard pattern of settlement went hand in hand with the universal acceptance of a common law and a common set of ideas about lordship, vassalage, service and tenure.

The new aristocracy was one of Royal Service and while some of the greatest lordships went to men who were given office in the king's household on a hereditary basis, others went to men who could be trusted and in return for their knight's feu would maintain law and order in their lands. Among the latter, the Fleming Freskin was made Lord of Strathbrock in West Lothian and later of Duffus in Moray. Many of the great nobles, including the native earls, imitated the example of the crown and set about forming knight's feus on their own estates. By the beginning of the 13th century much of south Scotland had already been distributed in knight's feus and the only scope for fresh creations was in the relatively unfeudalized earldoms in the north.

The native leaders or mormaers in the provinces of Scotland had roots which went far back in Scottish history. In most of Scotland, with the exceptions of Galloway, Fife, Gowrie, Angus, Mearns and Moray, the native nobility had been replaced. The mormaer of Fife could scarcely be termed a colonist, but about 1136 the Earldom of Fife was granted to Earl Duncan by royal charter. Duncan, being of the same kin as the king, had to hold his own amongst the Anglo-Norman nobles and quickly adapted to the system. The Earls of Fife became colonisers as avid as the many

133

foreign adventurers who flocked to Scotland to take advantage of royal favour. Their earldom consisted of a complex of estates between the Forth and the Tay, and as further lands were added by later kings, the Earls in turn rewarded their followers with knight's feus in their new lands (Barrow, 1980).

The men of Moray had been a thorn in the side of Scottish kings, clinging to their warlike ways. Successive kings had to march north to subdue these trouble-makers. The province of Moray in these times was much more extensive than the Moray of the present day, being bounded on the east and southeast by the River Spey from its mouth to near its source, then crossing the Great Glen west to Glen Garry, the boundary ran north along the watershed to Assynt and thence eastwards to the Dornoch Firth. In 1130, when King David was absent in England, Angus Earl of Moray rose in revolt but was defeated and slain at the Battle of Stracathro and his earldom forfeited. By settling men of his choice in Moray, David helped bring the province more firmly under the Scottish crown.

After the death of David, his successor Malcolm IV invaded Moray in 1160 and in the words of the historian Fordun "Removed tham all from the land of their birth and scattered them throughout the other districts of Scotland, both beyond the hills and on this side thereof, so that not a native of the land abode there, and he settled therein his own peaceful people." Some historians look on this as a major military intervention which ended the troubles: others maintain it was another stage in the replacement of the old troublesome landowners by chosen settlers and that it was only them who were driven out. Towards the end of the 12th century after the final pacification by the crown, Moray became available for more settlers and rewards were distributed for aiding King William. Duncan, the 2nd Earl of Fife and his son David were granted lands in Moray under this scheme (R.E.M. 16, 35, 62).

The first mention of Culbin in the historical records of Moray is when Richard de Moravia is referred to as being "de Culbin". His name appears in a charter dated 1235 in which King Alexander confirmed the transfer of lands in Sutherland to Richard as a gift from his brother Gilbert, Bishop of Caithness. These included the lands of Skelbo, near Dornoch. In the following year Richard was named in a charter as feuing Greater Kincorth and Little Kintessoch, which lay beside Culbin (R.E.M. 1837, p.464).

Shaw (1775) was of the opinion that Richard of Culbin was a descendant of Freskin de Moravia, but the family name "de Moravia" was very common at that time and there are several conflicting family histories. There is no question however, that Richard had close links with that family. The Freskins had helped King William against Harold Madaddson, Jarl of Orkney, who had invaded Caithness towards the end of the 12th century, and in return the king granted to Hugh, the eldest son of Freskin de Moravia, the lands of Sutherland, part of the Earldom of Caithness which had been forfeited. Hugh in turn gifted the lands of Skelbo to Gilbert de Moravia, Archdeacon of Moray under Bishop Bricius, on condition that the lands could only be passed to one of his own lineage. Hugh was succeeded by his eldest son William, and when the Caithness clans rose up and assassinated their bishop, the Freskins were again called on for help in putting down the rebellion. This they did, and William was created Earl of Sutherland. The new Bishop of Caithness was Gilbert de Moravia, and on taking up his charge in 1222 he gave the lands of Skelbo to his brother Richard de Moravia de Culbin. Richard later died at the Battle of Embo, normally dated as 1245, when aiding the Earl of Sutherland against invading Norsemen.

D. Murray Rose (1900, 1925) and quoted by Kinnaird (1982) had a different family tree, which he later modified as shown in notes preserved with his papers in Register House. He traced Richard of Culbin as being directly descended from the Earl Angus of Moray, who rose against King David in 1130. Angus's mother was a daughter of "king" Lulach, who had briefly succeeded his step-father Macbeth in 1057. In addition to lands in Moray, Angus had also held estates in the south. A charter granted in 1129 by King David confirmed the transfer of the lands of Newton in Fife by "My Lord Murray to Richard of Murray, his son". Angus was killed in the uprising of 1130 and his estates forfeited. The earldom of Moray was not revived until 1312 when Robert the Bruce granted it to his nephew Thomas Randolph for services in the defeat of the English. D. Murray Rose's succession down to Richard de Moravia de Culbin is given in Appendices 13 and 14.

Richard of Culbin married Marjorie de Lascelles, daughter of the sheriff of Fife, who brought lands at Naughton in the lordship of Newton in Fife to the Murray family. In addition to this Richard controlled the Barony of Culbin, Kindun, the Barony of Ethder and Calder in Strathclyde, Newton in Fife and Skelbo, Ferinbusca and Assynt in Sutherland. There is no indication as to when he came to Moray and settled in Culbin. Coming from Fife, he could have been involved with the Earl of Fife in aiding King William and got the lands in recognition of his services. Another possibility is his having been given the lands by Bishop Bricius or Bishop Andrew. Bricius, or Brice de Douglas, formerly Prior of Lesmahagow was Bishop of Moray from 1203–1222 and was the second son of William de Douglas, who had married a daughter of Freskin de Kerdal in Moray. During his time in office, he freely distributed church lands in Moray to his relations, including his four younger brothers who had come to Moray with him. His successor Andrew de Moravia was also a kinsman of the Freskins. While Richard's military prowess was no doubt useful in cementing powerful friendships, on the other hand, in these matters he was probably fulfilling his obligations to his feudal superiors.

From the days of Richard onwards, though only scattered pieces of information about the family exist, a succession can be established showing the Murray tree down to about 1418 (Appendix 14). His son, Sir Alexander Murray of Culbin is mentioned as granting a charter at his full court held at Newton in Fife in 1282. Alexander was succeeded by his son Alan and he in turn by his son Reginald. The Murrays had remained on good terms with the Earls of Sutherland and we find Kenneth, the 4th Earl, setting aside all claims to Reginald of Culbin's possessions in his earldom. Reginald was described as son and heir to the late Alan, *dominus de Culbyne*. Later in 1330 Reginald's son Gilbert married the Earl's daughter Eustacia (Fraser 1892). In 1389 Gilbert's grandson Alexander de Moravia de Coulbin stood as co-security for Lord Alexander, Earl of Buchan and Lord of Ross, not to mistreat the Lady Ross (Batten 1877). This Lord Alexander, better known as the "Wolf of Badenoch" was the second son of King Robert II who died in 1390. He had been ordered by the bishops to find security for his good behaviour towards his wife and took revenge by seizing lands belonging to the Bishop of Moray in Badenoch, only to be excommunicated by the bishop. Enraged, the Wolf and his followers descended on Lower Moray and sacked and burnt Forres and Elgin, destroying all the church property including the great cathedral of Elgin. Alexander of Culbin's name occurs in other surviving documents towards the end of the century. The continuing link with the Earls of Sutherland is shown by, when Strathnaver was plundered by the Macleods of Lewis, Earl Robert of Sutherland sent "Allister Neshram Gorme" (Alexander Murray of Culbin) with a company of men to stop the raiders. He caught up with them at Tuttim Tarwigh on the Ross-Sutherland border and killed all but one of them and recovered all the plunder (Gordon 1813). This battle took place about 1404.

Alexander was succeeded by his eldest son Thomas, who was described as a hero of Harlaw in 1411. He married Janet Maxwell of Pollock, getting a charter from his father of lands in Newton in Fife and Badfodelis in Aberdeen. He died in 1418 and was succeeded by his brother Angus (Murray Rose 1925). Angus claimed the Earldom of Moray, but was forfeited by the Duke of Albany and his estates given to Walter of Moray, who at one time was thought to have been the younger brother of Angus, but later considered to be the husband of Dame Mary Murray, Angus' sister. Angus was apprehended in 1427 by James I in Inverness and later released. The king had promised the estates of a Thomas Mackay, who had murdered the Laird of Freswick, to anyone who apprehended him, and Angus undertook this task. Knowing the family, he plotted with the two younger brothers, offering his two daughters in marriage if they helped. The plot was successful and Angus was rewarded for the capturing of Thomas by a grant of lands in Ross and Sutherland. (Reg. Mag. Sig. Vol II, No.149). Angus and the two brothers were later killed in a battle at Drum nan Coup near Tongue in 1433 (Gordon 1813).

Walter of Moray and Dame Mary Murray had three daughters, Egidia, Alison and Isobel. Egidia, sometimes known as Giles, was heiress to the lands of Culbin and married Sir Thomas Kinnaird ca. 1438.

# THE KINNAIRDS OF CULBIN

The family of Kinnaird also had a Flemish origin in a merchant Radulphus de Kynnard, who had received a charter of lands in the Carse of Gowrie in Perthshire sometime prior to 1184. This family continued successfully purchasing and receiving lands by marriage grants, in the east and northeast coastal regions of Scotland. The family became known as Kinnaird of that ilk in the late 14th century, controlling substantial estates (Kinnaird 1982). When Sir Thomas married Egidia Murray, the heiress of Culbin, their combined holdings of land were very extensive.

Thomas and Egidia had two sons, Alan and Thomas and a daughter Mariota. There was possibly another son Alexander, but there is no information on him other that this name appears on a charter as a witness in 1453 (SRO GD 125/6).

On the Friday before his assassination on the 21st February 1437, King James I received in his chamber within the Black Friars of Perth, the petition by Thomas Kinnaird and his wife Egidia, of the lands of Culbin, half of Nachtane, half of Badefodelis and Assynt, and sasine thereof to Alan, their son and heir (SRO GD 48/30.2). Following her husband's death, Egidia, on 12th May 1438, issued a revocation of the resignation, stating it had been related to the marriage being contracted between Alan and Margaret, daughter of the Lord of Grahame, but asserted that her agreement had been extracted from her "*per vim et metum*" on the part of her husband. In 1440 the trouble appears to have been resolved by the granting of the lands to Alan subject to his mother's life rent and other reservations.

In 1438 Mariota, Alan's sister, married Alexander Skene, son of James Skene of that ilk. In 1458 Egidia married her daughter's father-in-law, James Skene, at which point she transferred the estate of Skelbo to Alan. It is of interest to note here that Murray Rose (1925) stated that Egidia's mother had done a similar thing by marrying Alan Kinnaird, Egidia's father-in-law, after the death of her first husband, Walter of Moray.

According to Murray (1938a) Alan granted to his brother Thomas in 1466, the lands and barony of Culbin, Delputtie, Easterbin, Muirtown and Aikenhead, reserving for himself the life rent of Girseyards. This he did with the permission of his mother, and she reserved her life rent of all the lands. This may have been a method of providing for Thomas. Twelve years later, in 1478, Alan Kinnaird and Janet Keith his wife received a royal charter "under the white wax" of the barony of Culbin, presumably on the death of Thomas.

Alan Kinnaird died before March 1491, leaving two sons, Thomas and John. Thomas inherited the bulk of the estates while John, who had married Marjorie Mowat, received the lands of Skelbo. John died in 1494 and as he had no sons, the lands passed to Thomas, who was soon in litigation with his sister-in-law. For some reason he did not serve himself as heir to his father for ten years, during which time the estates lay in the king's hands. He had to pay compensation to Lord Andrew Grey on taking up his rights. He sold off the small detached properties of Over and Nether Tillieglens in Edinkillie parish in 1506 to John Calder, presentor of Rosse (SRO GD 248/32/5/1), while one third of the Mains of Culbin, formerly belonging to Elizabeth and Margaret Kynnard, daughters of his brother John, was resigned into his hands. His son Andrew received sasine of Skelbo in 1508.

Thomas died in 1514 and Andrew, the elder of his two sons inherited the estates of Skelbo, Kinnaird and Nachtane, while Walter, the second son, got Culbin. In 1525 Andrew's son John succeeded him. William Sutherland of Duffus, who had held a wadset on the lands of Skelbo against a loan of 1500 merks to John, acquired these lands in 1529 (Fraser 1892). From this stage onwards the lines of Culbin and Kinnaird steadily diverged.

Unfortunately the early records of the Burgh of Forres were destroyed, and while a few papers have survived from the first part of the 16th century, it is not until after about 1575 that any information can be gleaned from that source. Thereafter there was a general increase in available information, with historical records, council, church and kirk-session minutes etc. becoming more plentiful and detailed. It then becomes possible to build up a more general picture of the Kinnairds, as was done by Murray (1938a) in his history of the family. The latter part of the story of the Lairds of Culbin contains much more detail of the dealings and exploits of the family, and is not just a table of the line of succession and a list of properties controlled.

Many of the events in the family history from this point onwards have been related by Murray (1938a) but have been repeated here to put additional information into perspective.

On 12th September 1510 Thomas Kinnaird resigned to his second son Walter "... for good stead and service done and to be done to me, all and haill my barony of Culbin, with the teinds and tenantry of the same and 100 merks annually out of any lands in the lordship of Skelbo". Walter married (1) Marjory Dunbar, probably about this time as on 9th January 1511 the King confirmed to him and her in conjunct fee the lands of

Delpottie with the mill and multures thereof. He later married a Margaret Murray (Murray 1938a). He had a family of at least four sons whose names were listed in a precept dated February 1539: they were Alexander, George, Patrick and James. Alexander was to succeed his father in Culbin, George was in Laik, Patrick married Elizabeth Gordon and they were granted a charter by Bishop Patrick Hepburn of the lands of Salterhill, Mid Tulliebardin, Gedloch, Glenlatroquhy and Blairnahay. Nothing more is known of James.

Reference is made in sasines of a later period (1719 & 1725) of how in 1538 Alexander, Prior of Pluscarden, signed an agreement with Walter Kinnaird of Culbin and James Learmonth of Darsey on rights on peats and grazing in the mosses of Logie and Rough Carse (fig. 10, p.19 and fig. 23, p.109). This latter name was to appear in many documents under many guises brought about by misinterpretation of old handwriting—usually appearing as Ranchkers. Walter may have held some post with the Earldom of Moray as in 1540 he challenged the Elgin Burgh Court over a sentence passed on one of the Earl of Moray's officials and found himself in turn being charged with violating the jealously guarded rights of the Burgh. This was the last dated appearance of Walter.

He was succeeded by his eldest son Alexander who lived in the troubled times of the Reformation in Scotland which highlighted the deeply-felt religious differences between Catholics and Protestants: the former looking to France for a continuance of the "Auld Alliance" while the latter looked to England for help. Both countries provided aid in various forms, the French by providing a fleet and garrisons and the English sending armies—both in the name of the "true faith".

With Edward VI, a minor, on the throne of England, the staunchly Protestant Duke of Somerset was Regent. He marched over the border and soundly defeated the Scottish Catholics at Pinky Cleugh near Musselburgh. Among those killed were Alexander Kinnaird of Culbin and his cousin John Kinnaird of Kinnaird. Some neighbouring lairds from Morayshire were taken prisoner and later released on the payment of substantial ransoms.

Alexander Kinnaird had married Barbara Tulloch, daughter of the staunchly Catholic Alexander Tulloch, burgess of Forres and ancestor of the Tullochs of Tannachy. They had a son Walter who was a child at the time his father was killed. He spent his minority under the guardianship of his mother and nine years after Pinkie she and her father raised an action against the Sheriff of Moray for keeping her husband's estate tied up since his death. They failed to prove that they were the legal guardians and executors so the Lords found in favour of the sheriff. Walter eventually got possession of the estate of Culbin and in 1567, when in his early twenties, he followed Huntly south to support the Catholic cause, just as his father had before him. With the Earl of Bothwell having married Queen Mary, the rift between the Catholics and Protestants had widened sharply and their forces assembled at Carberry Hill not far from Pinkie. The supporters of Bothwell and Mary were commanded by Huntly and those of the opposition by James Stewart of Moray, Mary's half-brother. No battle ensued and Bothwell fled while Mary surrendered to the insurgent lords.

The Convention of Estates summoned Bothwell and his followers to appear on charges of treason. Among them were Patrick Hepburn, the last Catholic Bishop of Moray, who had sheltered Bothwell, several of his natural sons and diverse others including Walter Kinnaird and his uncle Thomas Tulloch. (*Acts of Parliament 1567*). Patrick Hepburn was Bishop of Moray from 1534–1573 and held with that appointment the Abbey of Scone. He was highly licentious and had an illegitimate family of at least nine who were eventually legitimised and all of whom he provided for out of the church properties. He also dispensed church lands to other relatives and friends and almost all the charters of alienation in the appendix of the *Moray Chartulary* (R.E.M.) were granted by him. Walter Kinnaird and his wife Elizabeth Innes and Patrick Kinnaird of Salterhill benefited in this way as did Kinnairds in other branches of the family in Fife.

In 1570 Walter granted the lands of Laik to his uncle Patrick and little more is heard of him until he attended a mustering of the local militia at Kilbuyak in the parish of Alves on the 8th of February 1596. Here the local lairds and their armed followers were reviewed. "The Laird of Culbin appeared on horseback, armed with a jack, steelbonnet, platesleeves, hagbut, spear and sword. He was accompanied by his eldest son and heir, Alexander, similarly accoutred, with six footmen wearing steel bonnets and bearing lances or other such weapons, two of whom were fit to serve the King abroad, the rest 'nocht abill' to serve without the country". With their religious feelings never far from the surface, Walter and his son Thomas were cautioned in 1600 "... not to reset Alexander Innes, minister of Birney, who has been denounced as a rebel" (Crammond 1903). The Kinnairds had a long standing feud with Samuel Falconer owner of the neighbouring property of Kincorth and both had to sign bonds for their mutual good behaviour. Walter had to sign for Alexander his son and heir, William Dunbar of Braco, his son in law, and for a number of tenants and servants, not to harm Falconer conform to the King's letter of 10th July 1610. Five months later the above mentioned, with Walter, William, Thomas and John Kinnaird, sons of the Laird, petitioned the Privy Council to have the amounts of their cautions reduced, as being excessive and beyond what the law prescribed. Culbin himself was described as "but a mean barron of a verie small rent", his sons and his son-in-law "unlanded gentlemen" and the others but poor cottars and tenants of

Figure 28     Gravestone preserved in Dyke Church.

Culbin. Kincorth's procurator excused the tenants but insisted on Walter senior, Alexander Kinnaird and William Dunbar finding security of £1000 Scots each and that of Culbin's other sons at £500 each. Murray (1938a) stressed that £1000 of caution was much less than the amount usually imposed upon landed proprietors in apparently similar circumstances and should be borne in mind by those tempted to overestimate the value of the Culbin estate before the great sand drift.

In the church of Dyke there is preserved a gravestone that was found in a heap of rubbish in the churchyard around 1823. The stone is in good condition and bears the names of Walter Kinnaird and Elizabeth Innes. On the upper part are engraved the coats of arms of the two families, the initials, VK and BI and the date 1613, with an inscription below (fig. 28, p.143). The heraldry of the Kinnairds of Culbin is discussed by Kinnaird (1982). Murray (1938a) presumed that Elizabeth Innes had died in that year, but later documents showed her to be still alive in 1629 but probably died before 1632.

The small estate of Easterbin, which had been part of the barony of Culbin until around 1600, had been acquired by a family of Dunbars. The income from fishing was an important part of the assets of any estate, and with Easterbin went the right to have a white-fishing boat which was crewed by the villagers from the Hill of Findhorn, a small community on the west shore of Findhorn Bay. In 1620, while Walter Kinnaird, the third son of the Laird of Culbin, had a wadset on Easterbin, Robert Dunbar's tacksman built a corfehouse in which to salt and pack fish, only to have it destroyed by Walter Kinnaird and estate workers from Culbin. They "came to the corfe house, armed with swords, spades, schell axes and other weapons: broke down the said house, cut the turfs and timber into small pieces and levelled the whole place equal with the ground". After Robert Dunbar's complaint, his case against Walter Kinnaird was heard by the Lords of Session in Edinburgh, who found for Walter. Only one of the witnesses called for Dunbar turned up, and those who failed to do so were denounced as rebels. It is probable that the outcome of the case was influenced by the fact that Walter Kinnaird held a wadset on the estate and might therefore claim the fishings, but the absence of the witnesses would not have helped. Robert Dunbar repaid the loan, which amounted to 2500 merks, on 25th April 1625.

That the Laird of Culbin was still well off is shown by the fact that at least five of his six sons moved into farms of their own: Alexander followed his father in Culbin, James in Whitewreath, Walter in Rait, William in Cassieford (later to become provost of Forres), John, after owning various salmon fishings and holding a wadset on Hempriggs, moved into that property. Nothing is known of Thomas, other than his name appearing in various documents as occasionally being in minor trouble with the church and in 1621 facing a charge of assault and robbery (Crammond 1903). The only daughter, Janet, married William Dunbar of Braco.

Alexander Kinnaird was served heir to his father on 4th April 1626, so on his death, Walter must have been in his 80s. Alexander got the superiority of Cowbin in the following year on the payment of £40, the right having been in crown hands for one year. Murray (1938a) stated that Alexander Kinnaird died in 1630 and that his eldest son Walter had married Grisselle Brodye on 20th August 1629, by her having at least three sons and two daughters and later marrying as his second wife Helen Forbes, widow of Baron Elphinstone on 19th March 1644. Murray's account of this period in the family's history is very inaccurate.

In a charter from Alexander to his eldest son Walter, mention is made of a marriage contract dated 14th April 1626, between Walter and Magdalen Dunbar, daughter of Martin Dunbar of Grangehill. Murray (1938b) makes no mention of this Magdelen in his history of the Dunbars of Grangehill. Walter Kinnaird and his wife Grisselle Brodye got the tenancy of the lands of Culbin etc. in 1629 while Walter's parents were still alive. Alexander maintained the life rent of Laik and Sandifield and reserved the superiority of the Manse of the Chapel of St Ninian, while Walter's grandmother, Elizabeth Innes, who was still alive, got an annuity of 24 bolls victuals. Murray (1921b) referred in a lecture to the mention in 1630 of a Patrick Kinnaird of Culbin. The source of this was probably the complaint to the Privy Council by a Margaret Bruce that Alexander Dunbar, son of William Dunbar of Braco and Janet Kinnaird, had attempted to murder her on the Mure of Tarrass, but that Patrick Kinnaird of Covine happening to come along at that time had succoured her. This was probably Patrick Kinnaird of Wester Alves and later of Glenlatroch, and the lady had mistakenly grouped all the Kinnairds as being of Culbin. Patrick could not have been the laird of Culbin as both Alexander Kinnaird of Culbin and Walter Kinnaird, fiar thereof, attended the trial.

Griselle Brodye had died before 1632, as in that year Marjorie Erskine was named in a sasine as "future spouse" to Walter Kinnaird and was granted life rent of the lands of Culbin etc. with permission of Walter's father, Alexander. On 12th January 1635, Helen Forbes received sasine of the lands of Culbin with permission of Walter's father. She was referred to as "nunc spouse honorabilis vir Walter Kinnaird de Cowbin". From the Parish Register for Dyke and Moy, a daughter Margaret born to Helen on 5th of January the following year, died when not quite 3 months old, and on 27th March 1639 another daughter Helen was born but died on 9th July of that year. The chronological order of the births of Walter's family by his four wives is in doubt, but their names and histories can be traced. As is seen from the accounts of other landed families, there seemed to be no difficulty for the lairds in getting new wives, but child birth seemed more hazardous than the battlefield and what the prospects were for wives and infants in the squalor of the cottar houses we can only guess.

In 1642 Walter Kinnaird received a charter from King Charles I to the estate of Culbin and on 19th March 1644 Helen Forbes received sasine of life rent to part of the estate. This was a re-affirmation of the charter granted in 1635 when she married Walter, who after getting the 1642 charter (presumably on the death of his father), was now the feudal superior. This was not as Murray suggested, the date of their marriage.

The feud between the Kinnairds and the Falconers of Kincorth seemed to have been settled, when in 1635 Walter granted to Samuel Falconer and his son William, hereditary sasine of the Manse of the Chapel of St Ninian, the feudal superiority being maintained by the Kinnairds. William Falconer was Samuel's illegitimate son, and had got Kincorth from his father in 1625. He was legitimised in 1629 and had become the minister of Dyke. It is debatable whether the gift was made in good faith, or because the Kinnairds, while quite happy to be enemies of a neighbour, feared the power that William would have in the parish now that he was the minister.

A few years later in 1642, the Kinnairds were involved in more feuding, this time probably arising out of differences in local politics. Walter Kinnaird had obtained a decree from the Sheriff of Moray against one of the local magistrates, Francis Forbes of Thornhill, but Forbes had appealed to the Lords of Council and the decree was suspended. The next day, Walter Kinnaird, accompanied by his uncle Walter Kinnaird of Rait and his son James, Provost William Kinnaird another uncle, two cousins Alexander and William Dunbar of Braco and others, met at the Provost's house in Forres and when Forbes passed by they rushed out with pistols and drawn swords and attacked him. Alexander Dunbar led the attack— he was no stranger to trouble, having been involved in the affair with Margaret Bruce in 1630 and had only recently returned to the district after an absence of several years during which he was a fugitive from justice, having killed one of his cousins from Hempriggs in a drunken brawl in 1636.

Forbes was rescued by some of the local people and made his escape. The Kinnaird gang, now joined by the Sheriff Alexander Dunbar, searched the town for Forbes, and failing to find him attacked others who had helped him. The townspeople gathered before the provost's house demanding he restore law and order. This he refused to do, and as might be expected the Laird of Culbin's version of the story was that he was at the Provost's house when Forbes led a party which attacked the house, trying to force an entry. The sequel to the tale is that at the next election William Kinnaird and his friends were ousted from the council and Francis Forbes became Provost.

Over this period the family fortunes continued to flourish. In 1631

Walter Kinnaird had acquired salmon fishing rights on the River Findhorn from James Spens of Kirktown of Alves. This stretch was known as the Common or Sheriff's Stell and meant that with his Easter and Wester Stells of Culbin he controlled the salmon fishings on the left bank of the river from where it left Findhorn Bay to the sea (fig. 23, p.109). The income from the fishings was a least as large as the estate grain rents.

In 1637 he stood as guarantor for his friend Sir Alexander Innes of Cockstoun in a deal involving the lands of Sherestoun. In 1644 Sir Alexander failed to keep his side of the bargain and dispossessed the family in Sherestoun, failing to pay them the 7,500 merks due to them. When a court case eventually came up, the Commissioners gave judgement against Walter Kinnaird as cautioner to the sum owed plus interest and costs amounting in total to 9950 merks. Walter then obtained a charter of the lands of Clackmarras from Sir Alexander Innes on 7th November 1652 and transferred these lands to the dispossessed William Chalmers in part payment.

Meanwhile in 1649 Walter had been loaning money to William Cumming against part of his lands of Earnside and Ordies and in 1651 increased his holding by taking over a loan made to Cumming by Lt. Col. Lachlan Ross. He obtained a further charter in 1655 which included the additional lands of Incheberie, Elljey, Ordechuisse, salmon fishing on the Spey, the lands of Meikle Phorpe and its mill and pertinents.

In 1654 Walter sent his son John to Edinburgh to stay with a friend, James Abernethie an advocate, and to be placed as an apprentice to a "writer". (Copies of three letters from Walter Kinnaird to the Abernethies appeared in the *Forres Gazette* of 12th December 1867, after John Martin had given a lecture on the Culbin Sands: their source was not recorded). In one of them dated 18th October 1655, the Laird of Culbin asked that the payment of moneys owed to Abernethie be put off till the term or a little later. As he could not make payment then, he suggested that in the meantime Abernethie use his bill as an I.O.U., a practice which was common in a land where there was little coin in circulation. This could be the first indication of a change in the fortunes of the family, but with grain rents being paid traditionally by the term of Candlemas, (2nd February), such a wait could be quite normal.

In 1660 Walter came into possession of the lands of Braco and its pendicle Paulruggatie, presumably on the death of his Dunbar cousins. These lands he quickly sold to John Falconer of Tulloch who was buying up land in that area at the time. Braco and Over and Nether Blairie had been owned as one unit up to 1581. Walter then obtained sasine on part of the lands of Longmoregone in life rent for himself and in free for his second son John. In 1664 he rented lands of Ordinghuis from Sir Alexander Abercrombie of Birkenbog—the year of John's marriage to Violet Abercrombie, Sir Alexander's daughter. Three years later John and Violet were granted the lands of Montcoffer by Sir Alexander.

These were troubled times for Scotland and the differences between the Royalists and supporters of the Covenant again erupted into open conflict. During his campaign in the North East, Montrose marched through Moray in 1646, charging all men between 60 and 16 to rise and serve the king under pain of fire and sword. Those who did not answer the call had their property plundered and burned. Although Walter Kinnaird was a Catholic and supported the king, he was treated no differently from his neighbour, the Laird of Brodie, whose sympathies lay with the other camp, and both their estates were burned. Walter was, in addition, made to contribute a forced loan of £333: 6s: 8d by the *Committee of Process and Moneys*, yet in 1651 when Montrose was being taken as a prisoner from Assynt to Edinburgh, the Laird of Culbin was one of a party of friends and admirers who accompanied him through Moray.

This period was one of great hardship in Moray, during which the estates and property of all Covenanters were ravaged and the town of Elgin plundered. This and the widespread acts of treachery and double-dealing were indelibly engraved on the memory of the people, and during the later changes in the monarchy, as power swayed back and forth between the two factions, revenge was extracted on both sides. While there was a Catholic king on the throne, Acts of Parliament named Walter Kinnaird as being on the Committee of War for the Shires of Elgin, Forres, Nairn and Inverness in 1648–9, while his son Thomas was Commissioner for Brunt and Waste Lands in Inverness-shire. After the Restoration, Walter was made Commissioner for Excise for Elginshire in 1661 and in 1667 Commissioner of Supply, and Thomas was given the same post in 1678, the year after he officially succeeded to his father's estates. The maintainance of law and order in these times was very difficult and Murray (1938a) related how when Sir Robert Innes of Innes, Hugh Rose of Kilravock and Thomas Kinnaird had been commissioned by the Privy Council to apprehend two law-breakers from Petty, with a view to their appearing on trial in Edinburgh, they were pursued and repeatedly harried by other members of the clan.

In May 1679 a band of Covenanters murdered Archbishop Sharp of St Andrews and a month later in Rutherglen a mob publically burned Acts of Parliament which legislated against the Presbyterians. Fearing a revolt, the Privy Council called out the militia, including those of Moray, to assemble at Stirling. Kinnaird's neighbours, who were largely Covenanters were in a quandary. Brodie of Lethen produced a letter from his daughter which warned him that the Macdonalds were preparing to march into Moray from the west. he advised his fellow lairds to stay at home to guard the country. This most of them did, but while Kinnaird, his son and several servants went south to join the king's forces, it is doubtful if they reached Stirling in time to join in the Battle of Bothwell Brig on 22nd June. At the enquiry which followed, charge and countercharge were made about the origin of the reports of a rising in the west. Two years later in 1681, an Act of Parliament enacting the "Test" was passed, which made it obligatory for all officials in Church and State to acknowledge that "The King's Majesty is the only supreme Governor over the realm", over all persons and in all causes as well ecclesiastical as civil. Thomas Kinnaird, as Commissioner of Supply, clearly had no hesitation in taking the test. The adherence of James Brodie of Brodie to the Covenant led to his being fined the enormous sum of £24,000 Scots in 1685; others of his relations were similarly treated.

# THE DECLINING FORTUNES OF THE KINNAIRDS

Back at the Barony of Culbin all was not going well for the Kinnairds, and for the first time we see a Laird of Culbin borrowing money rather than lending it. In 1667 Walter Kinnaird had rented out the salmon fishing of his Easter Stell to John Dawson of Findhorn for an annual rent of 1000 merks and four barrels of salmon. Two years later Dawson held the rights of both the Easter and Wester Stells of Culbin on a wadset of 2000 merks. Patrick Cumming had inherited his father's lands of Earnside and redeemed the wadset of 3050 merks held by Walter Kinnaird on the lands on 25th March 1673. On the next day Walter granted the lands of Delpottie and Earnhill with a garden called Netherbol, along with the Mill of Delpottie with thirlage, multures etc. to William Dunbar of Kintessack on a redeemable wadset of 8500 merks (Wm. Dunbar was later to become Sir William of Durn). Whether these sums of money were needed to pay off other debts is not known as Walter died on 24th October of that year (Brodie 1863).

Walter Kinnaird died in 1673 and the estate lay in the hands of the crown because of non-payment of feu duties. His son Thomas could not gain possession until this was paid off. Thomas' brother, John of Montcoffer, had died in 1669 leaving a widow and three children. His lands were confirmed to Walter, the eldest son with life-rent of the lands going to his widow. When his mother died in 1676, young Walter was only 9 years old, and the estate was administered by his uncle James Kinnaird.

The boy's maternal grandfather, Sir Alexander Abercrombie of Birkenbog had originally owned the lands, and he and his brother John now arranged to sell the farms to John's son-in-law, in spite of the questionable legality of such a deed. The proceeds, 10,000 merks, were then paid to Thomas Kinnaird of Culbin as the children's nearest relative, and the money was to be applied for their benefit. With this injection of capital there was a temporary improvement in Thomas' affairs. In 1677 his son married, he redeemed a wadset held on his fishings on the Findhorn, and he finally gained possession of his father's lands of Culbin after a delay of four years—presumably on payment of the overdue taxes. He also paid certain moneys to his brother James as his share of the estate.

149

There had for long been a shortage of peat for fuel in Lower Moray and it seems that Thomas Kinnaird coveted his neighbour's peat moss. In 1680 Brodie entered in his diary that Thomas Kinnaird and his servants moved into the peat moss on the Brodie side of their common boundary and proceeded to cut peats. Brodie then had the peats removed, but things were then made worse by Culbin building a house on Brodie's land. Then, on 26th July Brodie found that his cut peats were being stolen and two days later James Kinnaird, brother of the Laird of Culbin, made "civil interruption to the leading of the peats". Subsequent meetings between the two lairds, even with the Bishop of Moray as intermediary, failed to produce a solution to the problem, which on the face of it seemed quite a simple one. The Brodies had for some time been uneasy about the general behaviour of the Kinnairds and they were never mentioned in good light in Brodie's diary. In the autumn of the following year Brodie mentioned that Young Culbin had committed riots on a journey to Perth and then in 1682 wote "I heard of Culbin's debts and continuing difficulties, and their profanity that their daughter was with child." Murray (1938a p.33) suggested that this profanity could have been caused by the thought of the additional burden of a dowry being heaped on their mounting load of debts. In spite of these thoughts the two lairds still associated, though perhaps not quite voluntarily. Before Brodie's diary came to an end in 1685, there are several entries where Brodie lamented how easily and often he was drawn into drinking bouts with the Kinnairds.

At a meeting of the Inverness Town Council at the beginning of 1682 when contributions were being sought towards the building of a new bridge, it was indicated that this would be the last opportunity they would have of getting anything from the Laird of Culbin. On the 17th April Baillie William Duff, a merchant in Inverness, held the lands of Middlebin and the salmon fishings of the Culbin estate on a wadset. As mentioned earlier, letters of credit changed hands freely in the absence of currency, and later that year Baillie Duff, probably by collecting the wadsets held by others, obtained sasine on the entire estate in his own name, and this he held against a sum of 25,000 merks. One provision made was that no further sasines were to be taken on the lands of Culbin. The arrangement was made with the agreement of Helen Forbes, Thomas' mother, Anna Elphinstone his wife and Anna Rose his daughter-in-law, all of whom had been granted life rents from parts of the estate.

Murray stated that Thomas Kinnaird died in 1691, when according to the *Dyke Parish Register* he died on 3rd July, 1687, the 1691 date being when Alexander inherited the estate.

In 1689 the pendulum of succession to the throne had swung back in favour of the Protestants and William and Mary now reigned. Many acts introduced since 1660 depriving Protestants of their posts and privileges were repealed—a situation which did not go down well with those now out of favour. Viscount Dundee called the Scots Catholics to arms in a vain attempt to change matters by force, and in a proclamation issued on 18th July 1689, Dundee and his leading supporters were denounced as rebels and association with them declared to be high treason. The list included Alexander Kinnaird of Culbin and Innes of Coxton among those from Moray (Balfour Melville 1954). There was also a description of how, in 1690, Thomas Tulloch, brother of the Laird of Tannachy, being in the company of Kinnaird of Culbin and others in their cups, found dissatisfaction with the present government. Arguing on whether or not it was possible for the late king to return to the throne, Tulloch in a rage lifted his pistol and said "May this pistol be my death if he does not return again!" The pistol went off and shot him dead, much to the wonderment of the onlookers. Prebble (1968) states that Alexander Kinnaird was an officer in the Jacobite army that rose against William but had been pardoned in 1693.

The 1690s were the years of continuing crop failure and famine in Scotland. This following on the other financial troubles of the Laird of Culbin meant that there was little chance of his ever paying off his creditors. Baillie Duff realizing this, brought an action in the Court of Session against Alexander Kinnaird and obtained a decreet of adjudication against him. The transcript of this action is preserved, with all the properties of the estate listed as in the 1682 sasines. Fraser Mackintosh (1865a) described a rental of the estate for the year 1693 which he said was produced at the trial but is not now with Duff's litigation. This document has been quoted without question by almost every author who has written on the Culbin Sands and from this arose the legend of the fabulously wealthy estate. The rentals are discussed in detail elsewhere in this book (p.105).

In 1695 Alexander Kinnaird petitioned Parliament for relief from cess as the best two parts of his estate had been overblown with vast heaps of sand. After considering the matter, Their Lordships passed on the petition to the Lords Commissioners of the Treasury "to do in the matter as they find just." Murray (1938a p.39) stated that Alexander Kinnaird was granted relief from cess on the two thirds of the estate that was overblown, but that payment had to be made on the remaining third. The record of his appeal appears in the *Acts of Parliament* but documentary evidence of the Treasury's decision could not be traced. In 1695 an Act of Parliament was passed forbidding the pulling of bent, broom or juniper off sand hills and quoted the problems at Culbin.

With his creditors still harassing him, the estate was finally put up for public auction in July 1698 and bought by William Duff who then passed it on to his second son, Alexander Duff of Drummuir in the November of that year. Alexander Kinnaird granted a disposition of the estate on 27th July and in the document it was stated that the price paid, £20,259:10s: 6d Scots was fully £6000 less than the amounts due to William Duff and Sir James Abercrombie of Birkenbog, the only preferential creditors. Kinnaird acknowledged receipt of a sum of money from the Duffs out of goodwill and kindness. Probably as a result of this, those still holding his now worthless I.O.Us. again pressurised the Laird of Culbin for payment and he had to appeal to Parliament for protection against the creditors. He stated that by then three quarters of his lands had been overblown and the remainder sold off. He was granted the protection, Their Lordships decreeing that his debts were largely the result of an act of God. A final sasine of the lands was received by Alexander Duff in 1702.

Creditors who lost money included Alexander Forbes, Minister of Dyke, Sir James Calder of Muirtown, Alexander Hay, merchant in Elgin, Alexander Dunbar of Barmuckity, provost of Inverness, Walter Kinnaird eldest son of John Kinnaird of Mountcoffer, Patrick Tulloch of Bogtown, and Sir William Dunbar of Durn.

# THE LAST OF THE KINNAIRDS OF CULBIN

Of the early accounts of the final saga of the Kinnairds of Culbin, only brief and scattered versions have survived —some conflicting, most innacurate and all incomplete. Later accounts were almost all repeats of Bain's (1911) version: some quoted *verbatim*, but many with additional embroidery.

The oldest history of the "Family of Culbin" was by R. Grant of Kincorth, and appeared as appendix LV to Shaw's *History of Moray* (1827). In this, talking of Alexander, the last laird, Grant says, "He married Mary, daughter of Alexander, 10th Lord Forbes, and relict of Hugh Rose of Kilravock, by whom he had a son named Thomas (Parish Register of Dyke), who was a young child, and left orphan at the time the estate was destroyed. A female relation took charge of him, removed him to Edinburgh, where she supported herself and him for two years by needlework, until a half-brother of his, Col. Alex. Rose of a regiment of Horse stationed in Ireland, took him under his care. The young man himself afterwards became Captain of a troop of Horse, and died about the year 1743."

Fraser-Mackintosh (1865a), in his history of the estate, says (p.320) that Alexander Kinnaird finally signed over the remainder of his estate on 27th July 1698, and that in a document dated 16th November of that year, he was described as "then deceased". He left a son Alexander, who died without issue, and thus after 300 years possession, the Kinnairds of Culbin disappeared. [In the 1702 sasine which followed, the term used is "nuper de Culbin" = lately of Culbin].

The most frequently quoted authority on the Culbin estate is undoubtedly George Bain (1888, 1911, 1922, 1928). His account of events over this period states that Alexander Kinnaird was married to the daughter of Rose of Clava, and had just come into possession of the estate when it was overwhelmed. At this time their only boy was but a few months old. On the night of the catastrophe Alexander Kinnaird escaped with his wife and child, accompanied by a nurse. Both the laird and his wife died a few years later. The faithful nurse took the child to Edinburgh and supported him and herself by needlework. The lad, when grown up, enlisted in the army and was later recognised by his uncle, Col. Alexander Rose, who procured a commission for him. He rose to be Captain of a troop of Horse, and died without issue ca. 1743. In his 1928 account, Bain, presumably having in the meantime read *The History of Kilravock*, states Alexander Kinnaird died in Darien and that his widow lived to an advanced age. The son, unnamed, he promotes to Major.

Commenting on the reluctance of editors to exercise a degree of discretion before publishing fantastic legends which have been repeated *ad nauseum*, Murray (1938a) points out that Alexander Kinnaird married twice: first to Anna Rose of Clava and second to Mary Forbes, widow of Hugh Rose, the 14th Laird of Kilravock. The first marriage he describes as childless, and that the second produced one son, Alexander. As far as this lad's having been looked after by a nurse after the early death of his parents, Murray directs his readers to the *History of the Kilravock Family* (Rose, 1848) where Alexander Kinnaird is stated to have died in Darien and that Mary Forbes was alive in 1715. In a letter written in 1715 she referred to meeting her son Arthur Rose in London in that year. Murray then adds, "the life rent jointure of a laird of Kilravock's widow—however irregularly and sometmes incompletely paid—must have been sufficient to keep the wolf from the door". Murray does not dispute Bain's account of the lad's having had a successful career in the army, but points out that because Col. Alexander Rose was, in fact, the young Kinnaird's step-brother, the "recognition" was more than chance.

Looking at this part of the story in more detail, we find that Mary Forbes, as the second wife of Hugh Rose, the 14th Baron of Kilravock, bore him six sons: Alexander, Charles (who died in infancy), William, George, Arthur and John. The eldest of these, Alexander, had a distinguished career in the army, and was the Col. Alexander Rose who "looked after" the "orphaned" Kinnaird. On the death of the 14th Baron in 1687, his eldest son Hugh, by his first marriage, became the 15th Baron. A few years later in 1694, Mary Forbes married Alexander Kinnaird. Their son Thomas was born in 1695, and there is no indication as to why Murray refers to the lad as Alexander, as the *Dyke Parish Register* of 17th October 1695 clearly shows the son of Alexander Kinnaird and Mary Forbes to have been christened Thomas. Equally strangely, no early author mentions Alexander Kinnaird's family by his first wife, Anna Rose: three sons and two daughters.

Little is known of the last two years of Alexander Kinnaird's life, save the mention in the Kilravock History that he died in Darien. This is also referred to by Prebble (1968) in his account of the Darien Scheme.

As the 17th century drew to a close, Scotland was in desperate straits due to the famine brought on by 7 successive years of crop-failure. The Darien Scheme, which was the attempt to set up a trading company in a colony in Central America in 1698 is vividly summed up by Prebble

(1968). "The first attempt to make a company, a joint Scots and English version, was crushed by the English Parliament. The Scots created it by themselves, in a wave of almost hysterical enthusiasm, subscribing half the nation's capital. Three years later the 'noble undertaking', crippled by the quarrelsome stupidity of the leaders, deliberately obstructed by the English government, and opposed in arms by Spain, had ended in a stunning disaster. Nine ships owned by the company had been sunk, burnt or abandoned. Over 2000 men, women and children, who went to the fever-ridden colony, never returned. It was a tragic curtain to the last act of Scotland's independence."

Prebble had gleaned his information from the many published accounts listed in the bibliography to his book, but he had also been given access to many unpublished papers relating to the Darien Scheme. Probably quoting from one of the latter, he states: "At least one father was inflamed by the fire of his son's enthusiasm, and went with him. Alexander Kinnaird of Culbin had once been a Jacobite, an officer in the Highland Army that had risen against William, ten years before. Although he had been pardoned in 1693, his estate on the Moray Firth had since been engulfed by tidal sand. When his son was appointed an ensign in Capt. John Telfer's Company, he secured an overseer's commission for himself, and it may be that, in sharing the boy's life, he hoped to restore a tarnished name and a broken fortune."

Having abandoned their settlements to the Spanish, the Scots left in April 1700, and in the first week of May, three ships sighted the blue and green hills of Jamaica. Two hundred and fifty souls had died on this voyage. In the following two months, with little relief and no credit, another hundred died. These included "... The Laird of Culbin and his son Ensign William Kinnaird". In the index to Prebble's Darien Disaster he is referred to as "Kinnaird of Culbin, Sir Alexander."

Forbes (1975) gives a somewhat different account, stating "Sir Edward Kinnaird of Culbin, whose estate was completely covered in sand by 1698, had borrowed money from friends and had gone with the ships. He died in Darien, and his son reached America, never to return to Culbin. For many years the widow petitioned the King for help, as she was unable to pay the taxes demanded. No help was given, and she lived on the charity of relations." As in other parts of his book, Forbes does not give the sources of his information.

According to Shaw's description in the *Kilravock Family History*, Alexander Kinnaird's widow, Dame Mary Forbes "... was of unhappy temper, and has left too many records of her affairs, in those long sheets written or printed—the 'petitions', 'representations', 'memorials' of the old lawyers' practice, conveying little information now, nor exciting any interest, unless pity for a life spent and embittered in wrangling with her nearest friends." However, some information can be gleaned from these records.

That she was not on good terms with her stepson Hugh, the 15th Baron, is shown in *A public letter to Hugh Rose of Killraick* in 1723 (SRO GD125/31, GD 125/14/3), where she complains "For very near seven years you could find no occasion to deprive me of the small jointure I had: yet when by fatal advice in 1693 I was induced to make you my chamberlain, you took the fifth part of what you had given me as Aliment for six children your Father left me, for your Chamberlain's fee; tho' all I had for each child was but five pounds Sterling; This for Bed, Board, Clothes, Linnens, Schools, and Colleges.

When I was married in Cubine, in 1694, then you shew'd your kindness to me, and your Father's dear Friend: of whom he said in my hearing, Now Hugh, shake hands with Alaster; and if you do not stand and fall with him, God curse you: Instead of Obedience to that, you made him fall: and I still must say, I doubt not, but Darien will prove to you, what the sword of the Children of Ammon was to David: ... And to show your Sympathy with me, you told my Husband, that unless he would leave me, and shift for himself, you would do nothing: but if he left me, you would not let me want: You had marr'd his Project, and his Friend's Proposals, that were willing to further the Preservation of his estate. So drown'd out his Fire, and forced him and his sons to go to Darien: and thus what God had join'd, you separated. When he was gone, you sent for me North, where, instead of a hundred Pound yearly which my jointure ... might have yielded, your generous Offer was, 10 pounds Sterling or 300 Merks per Annum ..."

Her references to Alexander Kinnaird's *sons*, in the plural, sends one back to the *Dyke Parish Register*, where three births were recorded as children to Alexander Kinnaird and his first wife, Anna Rose: Alexander born 1680, Elizabeth born 1684 and Robert born 1685. The death of a daughter Anna in 1683 is also recorded but there is no date of birth. She may have been born in Nairn, as was her sister Elizabeth but in her case this was also recorded in the *Dyke Parish Register*. There is no mention here of the William mentioned by Prebble, but several pages from around this period are either torn or missing. That a William did exist is shown by his being a witness to two deeds in the *Rose Family Papers* (SRO GD125 Box 19) the first dated 1694 and the second, which describes him as "son to Alex^r, Kynaird of Cowbin, 1696". The entry for Alexander's christening is not in the usual form, there being an additional sentence after the normal record, which starts "This child was born and baptised..." but the remainder is illegible. This might be interpreted as meaning that the child had died. If so, this leaves the youngest son Robert as the one who, at the age of 14, had accompanied his father and brother to Darien.

On the other hand, this too could have been the additional note that the child had also been born and baptised at Nairn, which could also be the case for William.

As for the question as to who might have taken the "orphaned" Thomas Kinnaird to Edinburgh, and looked after him there, we have two versions: Grant, in Shaw (1827) refers to a female relative taking charge of him, while Bain, (1911) refers to a faithful nurse.

Mary Forbes was, no doubt, of the opinion that if Hugh Rose was ready to severely curtail the allowances due to herself and her five Rose sons out of the Kilravock Estate, he would be even less sympathetic towards the infant Thomas Kinnaird. Her harsh view of Hugh may not have allowed for the poor state of the estate when he inherited it (Rose 1848), nor for the effects the appalling weather conditions of the 1690s had had on the harvests of the period. These famine years meant that most Scottish landowners were in a bad way and many had to sell their estates for very low sums.

In Moray, many of the bankrupted estates were purchased by William Duff of Dipple, a banker and money-lender—a move which led to his amassing the largest fortune in the north of Scotland (Tayler and Tayler 1914) and paved the way for his eldest son to become the first Earl of Fife. He had been apprenticed to his uncle in Inverness, the Baillie William Duff who had brought the 1694 court case against Alexander Kinnaird, and together with their partner Sir James Calder of Muirtown, they controlled virtually all the foreign trade north of Aberdeen. Baillie Duff had purchased the Culbin estate in the name of his eldest son, Alexander Duff of Drummuir, in 1698.

Hugh Rose (15th) had been acquiring lands through marriage during this period (Rose 1848), had become a M.P. and subsequently married Sir James Calder's daughter Elizabeth, as his fourth wife. Sir James had not proved to be as astute in business affairs as his two partners and when he fell into debt Hugh paid his father-in-law's debts and acquired a right to the Barony of Muirtown—a move Shaw describes as so expensive that he lost rather than gained by it. Again it is possible that Mary Forbes, when writing her open letter years later, noted only Hugh's successes over the years and ignored his failures. However she blames him for thwarting Alexander Kinnaird's plans for the preservation of the Culbin estate, whatever they might have been.

That her 1725 letter states, "when you sent for me north..." can be interpreted as meaning that she and her husband had been living in the Edinburgh area during or after the period of the legal actions against him and his subsequent petition to Parliament. She quotes Hugh as saying to Alexander Kinnaird that unless he would leave her and shift for himself, he would not help them, pointing to his considering Alexander to be something of a parasite and quite happy to live on his wife's allowances. In Edinburgh Kinnaird would be well aware of the forthcoming Darien venture and no doubt saw it as an opportunity to make his fortune. Being on the spot he could organise his voyage in good time, but it is of interest to note that both William Duff of Dipple and his cousin Alexander Duff of Drummuir are listed among the company shareholders (Maclean 1900).

Once he had departed, Hugh Rose, keeping his side of the bargain, sent for Mary Forbes and her family. She may well have found it convenient to leave the Kinnaird boy with a relative in Edinburgh, whilst travelling north with the five young Roses, and once he had settled there, to leave him indefinately . This would provide the basis for the tales of an Edinburgh upbringing. The practice of "fostering" children with an elderly relative remained quite common into more recent times.

Some details of the career of Mary Forbes' oldest son, Alexander Rose, are to be found in the *Kilravock Family History* (Rose 1848). He seemed to have been on good terms with his half-brother Hugh, the 15th Baron, judging from the fact that in January 1728, in the inn in Findhorn, together they managed to consume 49 bottles of wine in the space of two days (Innes 1861). At some point, as the stories agree, Alexander Rose took his half-brother Thomas Kinnaird under his wing, and aided his career in the army.

In a list of the Officers of His Majesty's Forces on the Irish Establishment published in 1740, he is listed as a Lt. Col. in Lord Molesworth's Regiment of Dragoons, having first been commissioned as a Captain in 1704 and reaching the rank of Lt. Col. by 1729. In the same list appears Lt. Thomas Kynnard, first commissioned in 1735 and taking his rank as Lt. in 1739. (Scottish National Library Document GWB 72). The *Scots Magazine* of October 1742 p.487 lists, under Preferments, Thomas Kynaird, Adjutant to Molesworth's Dragoons. As such he appears in a list dated 1745, (*Public Record Office*, Kew. Ref WO 64/10), but is not in the next extant list dated 1752 (WO 64/11). No casualty lists appeared at that period, but if he was killed in hostilities associated with the '45, notice may have appeared in the Irish Papers of the time. Lt. Col. Rose is recorded as having died in 1743, but only an approximate date for Thomas' death can be given—ca. 1746. The Kinnaird Family Tree appears as Appendix 15.

# CONCLUSION

In conclusion it must be said that the origin and history of the Culbin Sands is a fascinating subject, and the large number of texts on the area uncovered during this study proved to contain a strange mixture of fact and fiction. The desert-like landscape had lent itself to mystery, and against that background, natural disasters, intrigue and family misfortunes had been quickly dramatised by early writers into a collection of legends which were repeated so often that today they are accepted as fact.

The tale of the most productive estate in the land being overwhelmed by a sandstorm in a single night and the sad fate of the laird and his family has stimulated people's imagination for nearly three centuries. Today the study of the geomorphology of the Culbin and of the climate prevailing at the time reveal a different tale—one of a progressive deterioration during many years of adverse weather conditions.

On the historical side in particular, while snippets of fact had been woven into the legends, the only way of checking them was to trace the original records from which they had been gleaned. This revealed that much of the information which could have been used to reveal the true nature of events had always been available for study, but had been ignored over the years.

Pointers leading to additional sources of information were also uncovered during the study, as were tantalising shreds of evidence which hinted that the Culbin has not yet given up all its secrets.

# EPILOGUE

Whilst researching into his own connection with the Kinnairds of Culbin, John Kinnaird, Secretary of the Scottish Genealogical Society, discovered in one of his Society's publications, (Angus Monumental Inscriptions Vol.1, p.283) that the entry for grave 106 in Newtyle grave-yard read: "1813 George Watson Esq., Bannantyne House w. Jean Rose, sole heiress of ancient families of Moray and Kinnaird of Culbin". Elizabeth Kinnaird, Alexander Kinnaird's surviving daughter married a Hugh Rose in Nairn on 12th November 1706. Since her brothers had died without issue, only descendents of Elizabeth could claim this unique ancestry, and, after all, nobody tries to trace the female line.

It is a fitting end to the tale that in spite of the legends, neither the estate nor the family really vanished without trace.

# BIBLIOGRAPHY

| ABERCROMBY C.D. | 1927 | *The Family of Abercromby*, Aberdeen. |
| ADAMS, I.H. (Ed) | 1979 | Papers on Peter May, Land Surveyor, 1749–1793: *Scottish History Society*, Edinburgh. |
| AITKEN, A.M. et al. | 1979 | The Sand and Gravel Resources of the Country around Garmouth, Grampian Region. *Institute of Geological Sciences*, Mineral Assessment Report 41. |
| AITKEN, M. | 1842 | Parish of Dyke and Moy. *Second Statistical Account of Scotland*, Edinburgh. |
| ALGIE, M.J. | 1887 | The Culbin Sands. In *Guide to Forres*, Forres. |
| ALLAN, J. | 1689 | *Memoirs*, Moray District Record Office. DBL 79/1. |
| ANDERSON, M. | 1938 | *The Culbin Sands*, Forres Gazette. |
| ANDERSON, M. | 1954 | The Sandhills of Culbin: in *Guide to Forres*, Perth. |
| ANNAND, J.F. | 1928 | Progress of Forestry Work on Culbin Sands, Morayshire, *Scot. For. Jl.*, 42, 8. |
| BAGNAULD, R.A. | 1954 | *The Physics of Blown Sand and Desert Dunes*, 2nd Edition, London. |
| BAIN, G. | 1882 | A Walk to the Culbin Sands: a lecture to the *Nairn Lit. Inst.*, Nairn. |
| BAIN, G. | 1911 | The Lost Barony of Culbin: in *The River Findhorn*, Nairn. |
| BAIN, G. | 1922 | *The Culbin Sands* or *The Story of a Buried Estate*, Nairn. |
| BAIN, G. | 1928 | *The History of Nairnshire*, Nairn. |
| BALFOUR-MELVILLE, E.W.M. | 1954 | An Account of the Proceedings of the Estates in Scotland, 1689–1690, *Scottish History Society*, Vol. XLVI, 3rd Series, (1). |
| BARROW, G.W.S. | 1980 | *The Anglo-Norman Era in Scottish History*, Oxford University Press. |
| BATTEN, E.C. | 1877 | *The Charters of the Priory of Beauly*, Grampian Club. |
| BLACK, G.F. | 1891 | Report on the Archaeological Examination of the Culbin Sands, Elginshire, *Proc. Roy. Soc. Antiq.* |

161

BOULTON, G.S. 1972 Modern Arctic glaciers as depositional models for former ice sheets, *Jl. geol. Soc. Lond.* 128, 361–393.

BREMNER, A. 1934 The Glaciation of Moray and Ice Movements in the North of Scotland, *Trans. Edin. Geol. Soc.* 13, 17–56.

BRODIE, A. 1863 *The Diary of Alexander Brodie of Brodie*, Aberdeen.

BRODIE-INNES, J.W. 1914 The Barony of Culbin: in *The Story of the Findhorn*, Forres Gazette.

BRODIE-INNES, J.W. 1915 *The Devil's Mistress*, London.

BURGESS, J.J. 1920 The Flora of Culbin, *Trans. Banff Field Club*.

BURGESS, J.J. 1935 *The Flora of Moray*, Elgin.

CALLANDER, J.G. 1911 Notice of the Discovery of Two Vessels of Clay on the Culbin Sands, *Proc. Soc. Antiq. Scot.*, 45, 158.

CHARLESWORTH, J.K. 1956 The Late-Glacial History of the Highlands and islands of Scotland, *Trans. Roy. Soc. Edin.* 62, 769–928.

CHESHER, J.A. & LAWSON, D. 1983 *The Geology of the Moray Firth*, I.G.S. Report 83/5. London, H.M.S.O.

CLARK, J.T. (Ed) 1900 *Genealogical Collections concerning Families in Scotland made by Walter Macfarlane, 1750–51*, Edinburgh.

COCHRANE, R.G. 1981 *Findhorn, a Scottish Village*, Forres.

COCHRANE, R.G. 1985 *Findhorn, A Scottish Village*, Revised 2nd Edition, Forres.

COLES, J.M. & TAYLOR, J.J. 1970 The Excavation of a midden in the Culbin Sands, *Proc. Soc. Antiq. Scot.*, 102, 87.

COURT OF SESSION 1760 *Brodie Vs. Dunbar, Findhorn Fishings Dispute*, Edinburgh.

CRAIG, G. 1880 Excursion to the Sandhills of Culbin, *Trans. Inverness Sc. Soc. & Field Club*, 1, 316.

CRAIG, G. 1888 The Culbin Sandhills, *Trans. Edin. Geol. Soc.* 5, 524.

CRAMMOND, W. 1903 *The Records of Elgin, 1234–1800*, Aberdeen.

DOBBIE, D.H. & PARTNERS 1966 *Report on Coastal Erosion at Findhorn*, Report to Moray County Council.

DONALDSON, J. 1794 *General View of the Agriculture of the County of Elgin or Moray*, Board of Agriculture.

DOUGLAS, R. 1934 *The Annals of Forres*, Elgin.

DUFF, P. 1842 *A Sketch of the Geology of Moray*, Elgin.

DUNBAR, J. 1799 Parish of Dyke, including the Annexed Parish of Moy, Moray. In *First Statistical Account of Scotland*, 1791–1799.

DUNBAR-DUNBAR, E. 1865 *Social Life in Former Days*, Edinburgh.

| | | |
|---|---|---|
| DUNBAR-DUNBAR, E. | 1895 | *Documents Relating to the Province of Moray*, Edinburgh. |
| DUNCAN, A.A.M. | 1975 | *The Edinburgh History of Scotland*, Vol.1, Edinburgh. |
| DYKE WOMEN'S RURAL INSTITUTE | 1966 | *A History of the Parish of Dyke and Moy.* |
| EDLIN, H.L. | 1976 | The Culbin Sands: in *Environment and Man*, Vol.4. Reclamation, London. |
| EWING, P. | 1912 | The Flora of the Culbin Sands: in *The Glasgow Naturalist*. |
| FENTON, A. | 1968 | Alternating Stone and Turf: an Obsolete Building Practice, *Folk Life*, 6. |
| FENTON, A. | 1976 | *Scottish Country Life*, Edinburgh. |
| FENTON A. & WALKER, B. | 1981 | *The Rural Architecture of Scotland*, Edinburgh. |
| FLEMING, N.C. | 1982 | Multiple Regression Analysis of Earth Movements and Eustatic Sea-level Change in the United Kingdom in the past 9000 years, *Proc. Geol. Assoc.* 93 (1), 113–125. |
| FORBES, A.H. | 1975 | *Forres—A Royal Burgh, 1150–1975*, Elgin. |
| FORBES, D. | 1864 | *Account of the Family of Innes*, Aberdeen. |
| FORESTRY COMMISSION | 1950 | *Britain's Forests: Culbin*, H.M.S.O., London. |
| FRASER, W. | 1892 | *The Sutherland Book*, Edinburgh. |
| FRASER-MACKINTOSH, C. | 1865a. | The Lost House of Culbin: in *Antiquarian Notes, Historical, Genealogical, etc.*, Inverness. |
| FRASER-MACKINTOSH, C. | 1865b. | *Rental of Bishoprick of Moray—1641*: op.cit. |
| GASKIN, J. | 1972 | *Culbin Coast Defence Measures*, Forestry Commission. |
| GAULD, J.H. | 1981 | The Soils of the Culbin Forest, Morayshire. Their Evolution and Morphology, with Reference to their Forestry Potential, *Applied Geography*,1, 199–212. |
| GORDON, G. | 1839 | *Collectanae for a Flora of Moray*, Elgin. |
| GORDON, G. | 1859 | The Geology of the Lower of Northern Part of the Province of Moray, *Edin. New Phil. Jl.*, Edinburgh. |
| GORDON, G. | 1889 | *The Fauna of Moray*, Elgin. |
| GORDON, R. | 1813 | *A Genealogical History of the Earldom of Sutherland*, Edinburgh. |
| GORDON-CUMMING, C.H. | 1884 | The Lowlands of Moray, *National Review*, 4, 642–57. |
| GORDON-CUMMING, E. | 1878 | The Sand Hills of Culbin: in *Ballads*, London. |
| GOUDIE, A. | 1981 | *The Human Impact*, Oxford. |

GRAHAM, C.                    1977    *A Portrait of the Moray Firth*, Robert Hale, London.

GRAHAM, H.G.                  1901    *The Social Life of Scotland in the 18th Century*, London.

GRANT, J. & LESLIE, W.        1798    *A Survey of Moray*, Elgin.

GRIGOR, J.                    1881    *Arboriculture*, 2nd Edition, Edinburgh.

HARDING, M.                   1986    A time of Smothering Sands, *Northern Scot*, Christmas Number. Elgin.

HENDERSON, T.                 1932    The Culbin Sands: in *The Findhorn*, London.

HOLFORD, I.                   1977    Sandstorms: *The Guinness Book of Weather Facts and Feats*, 80. London.

HORNE, J.                     1923    The Geology of the Lower Findhorn and Lower Strathnairn: *Mem. Geol. Surv.*

HUME-BROWN, P. (Ed).          1891    Thomas Tucker in Inverness and Murray in 1655: in *Early Travels in Scotland*, Edinburgh.

INNES, C.                     1861    *Sketches of Early Scotch History and Social Progress*, Edinburgh.

KELLY, K.                     1985    *Wildlife Oasis in Sand Dune Forest*, Forres Gazette. 3/4/85.

KINNAIRD, H.                  1982    *A Short History of the Scots Name Kinnaird*, Glasgow.

KYD, J.G. (Ed).               1952    Webster's Analysis of Population 1755, *Scottish Population Satatistics*, Edinburgh.

LAMB, H.H.                    1982    *Climate, History and the Modern World*, London.

LAMB, H.H.                    1991    *Historic Storms of the North Sea, British Isles and North West Europe*, Cambridge.

LAUDER, T.D.                  1830    *An Account of the Great Floods of August 1829, in the Province of Moray and Adjoining Districts*, Edinburgh.

LESLIE, W.                    1811    *General View of the Agriculture in the Counties of Nairn and Moray*, London.

LESLIE, W.                    1823    *A Manual of the Antiques, Distinguished Buildings and Natural Curiosities of Moray*, Elgin.

LINTON, H.                    1876    Notice of a Collection of Flint Arrowheads and Bronze and Iron Relics from the Site of an Ancient Settlement recently discovered in the Culbin Sands near Findhorn, Morayshire,*Proc.Soc.Ant.Scot.*XI,543.Edinburgh.

MACEWEN, D.K.                 1964    The Kinnairds and Culbin, *Northern Scot*, Christmas Number. Elgin.

MACFARLANE, W.                1723    Description of Duffus Parioch in Elginshire: in *Geographical Collections. Scottish History Soc.*, Edinburgh. (1906).

MACGREGOR, A.A.               1949    *The Buried Barony*, London.

| MACKAY, W. | 1915 | *An Inverness Merchant of Olden Time*, Edinburgh. |
| MACKIE, W. | 1897 | The Sands and Sandstones of Eastern Moray, *Trans. Edin. Geol. Soc.* 7, 148. |
| MACKINTOSH, H.B. | 1924 | *Pilgrimages in Moray*, Elgin. |
| MACKINTOSH, H.B. | 1928 | *The Lossie and the Loch of Spynie*, Elgin. |
| MACLEAN, J.P. | 1900 | *An Historical Account of the Settlements of Scotch Highlanders in America*, Glasgow. |
| MACPHAIL, S.R. | 1881 | *History of the Religious House of Pluscardyn*, Edinburgh. |
| MARTIN, J. | 1836 | The Geology of Morayshire, *Prize Essays and Transactions of the Highlands and Agricultural Society of Scotland*, 5, 417–40. |
| MARTIN, J. | 1856 | On the Northern Drift as it is developed on the Southern Shore of the Moray Firth, *Edin. Phil. Jl.*, New Series. Edinburgh. |
| MARTIN, J. | 1860 | *The Buried Estate of Culbin*, Elgin Courant, Elgin. |
| MARTIN, J. | 1867 | *The Sandhills of Culbin*, Forres Gazette. 18/12/1867. |
| MARTIN, J. | 1875 | *The Sands of Culbin*, Elgin Courant. 26/3/1875. |
| MATHEWSON, A. | 1878 | Notes on the Age of the Settlements on the Sands of Culbin, *Proc. Soc. Ant. Scot.* XII, 302. Edinburgh. |
| MILLER, H. | 1854 | *My Schools and Schoolmasters*, Edinburgh. |
| MILLER, H. | 1859 | *Sketch Book of Popular Geology*, Edinburgh. |
| MILLER, H.G. | 1969 | Nitrogen Nutrition of Pines on the Sands of Culin, Morayshire, *Jl. of the Science of Food and Agriculture*, 20, 417–19. |
| MOIRA & MOIRA | 1970 | *Findhorn Dune Area*, Report on Conservation and Development. |
| MORAY & NAIRN COUNTY COUNCIL | 1972 | *Report on Coastal Erosion: Burghead Bay, Culbin and Findhorn Bay.* |
| MORRISON, A.A. | 1976 | *The Flora of the Old Bar*, Nairn. Unpublished Thesis, University of Manchester. |
| MURDOCH, J.B. | 1893 | Notes on a Visit to the Culbin Sands, Morayshire, *Trans. Geol. Soc. Glasgow*, 9, (2). |
| MURRAY, J.G. | 1921a | *The Hill of Findhorn*, Inverness Courier, 25/1/21. |
| MURRAY, J.G. | 1921b | *The Barony of Culbin*, Elgin Courant 2/9/21. |
| MURRAY, J.G. | 1938a | *The Kinnairds of Culbin*, Inverness. |
| MURRAY, J.G. | 1938b | *The Dunbars of Grangehill*, Forres Gazette. |
| MURRAY, J.G. | 1938c | *The Mill of Moy*, Forres Gazette. |
| NATIONAL MUSEUM OF ANTIQUITIES OF SCOTLAND | 1892a | *General Index of Relics from the Culbin Sands*—Catalogue 1851–1890. |
|  | 1892b | *Special Collections in Scotland.* |

NOBLE, R.R. 1984 Turf-walled Houses of the Central Highlands: in *Folk Life*, 22.

OGILVIE, A.G. 1923 The Physiography of the Moray firth Coast. *Trans. Roy. Soc. Edin.* 53.2 (No.19).

OVINGTON, J.D. 1950 The Afforestation of the Culbin Sands. *Journal of Ecology*, 38, 303–19.

PATTON, D. & STEWART, E.J.A. 1914 The Flora of the Culbin Sands, *Trans. Bot. Soc. Edin.* 26, 345.

PATTON, D. & STEWART, E.J.A. 1923 The Vegetation of the Culbin Sands, *Bot. Exch. Cl.*

PATTON, D. & STEWART, E.J.A. 1924 Additional notes on the Flora of the Culbin Sands, *Trans. Bot. Soc. Edin.*, 29, 27.

PEACOCK, J.D. et al. 1968 The Geology of the Elgin District, *Mem. Geol. Surv.*

PEACOCK, J.D. 1971 A re-interpretation of the Coastal Deposits of Banffshire and their Place in the late-Glacial History of N.E. Scotland, *Bull. Geol. Surv. Gt. Br.*, No.37, 81–89.

PEACOCK, J.D. 1977 Surface deposits of Inverness and the Inner Cromarty Firth. In Gill, G. (Ed). *The Moray Firth Area: Geological Studies*, Inverness. 103.

PIRIE, J. 1884 The Sand Hills of Culbin, *Jl. of the Excursions of the Elgin and Morayshire Lit. & Sc. Assoc.* Elgin.

POCOCKE, R. 1887 Tours in Scotland, 1747, 1750, 1760, *Scottish History Society*, 1.

PREBBLE, J. 1968 *The Darien Disaster*, Edinburgh.

RAMPINI, C. 1897 *A History of Moray and Nairn*, Edinburgh.

R.E.M. 1837 *A Registrum Episcopatus Moraviensis*, Edinburgh.

READ, H.H. 1923 The Geology of the Country round Banff, Huntly and Turriff, *Mem. Geol. Surv. Scotland.* H.M.S.O.

RHIND, W. 1839 The Sands of Culbin: In *Sketches of Moray*. Edinburgh.

RITCHIE, J.B. 1932 The Vanished Ports of Findhorn. The Culbin Sands, in *The Pageant of Morayland*, Elgin.

RITCHIE, W. et al. 1978 *The Beaches of Northeast Scotland*, Dept. of Geography, University of Aberdeen.

ROBERTSON, M. 1842 Parish of Kinloss, Elginshire, *Second Statistical Account of Scotland* 1842.

ROSE, D.M. 1900 *The Sutherlands of Duffus and Skelbo*, Northern Times, Golspie.

ROSE, D.M. 1925 *The Murrays of Culbin, Kinnairds and Roses*, Nairnshire Telegraph.

| | | |
|---|---|---|
| ROSE, H. | 1848 | *The Family of Kilravock 1290–1847*, Edinburgh. (Extended by Lachlan Shaw 1753 and finally by Cosmo Innes). |
| ROSS, S.M. | 1974 | Notes on the Development of the Culbin Foreland, MFCP No.2. *Bull. Moray Field Club*, 2. |
| ROSS, S.M. | 1975 | Ancient Soils in the Culbin Forest, MFCP No.3. *Bull. Moray Field Club*, 3. |
| ROSS, S.M. | 1976 et seq. | Annual Reports on the Erosion of the Moray Coast: in *Bull. Moray Field Club*, Marked 'E'. |
| ROSS, S.M. | 1976 | The Physical Background: in Omand, D. (Ed), *The Moray Book*, Edinburgh. |
| ROSS, S.M. | 1976 | The Climate of Moray. Op. cit. |
| ROSS, S.M. | 1981 | The 'Costa da Sand' MFCP No.41, *Bull. Moray Field Club*, 9. |
| ROSS, S.M. | 1983 | All and heall the Barony of Culbin, MFCP No.57, *Bull Moray Field Club*, 11. |
| ROSS, S.M. | 1986 | Old Maps of Moray, MFCP No.76, *Bull. Moray Field Club*, 14. |
| ROSS, S.M. & MACFARLANE, T. | 1977 | A Marine Clay from Burghead Bay, MFCP No. 21, *Bull. Moray Field Club*, 5. |
| ROYAL SCOTTISH GEOGRAPHICAL SOCIETY | 1973 | *The Early Maps of Scotland*, Edinburgh. |
| SCOTT, A.H.A. | 1975a | Further Notes on the Barony of Culbin, MFCP No.7, *Bull. Moray Field Club*, 3. |
| SCOTT, A.H.A. | 1975b | *Laigh of Moray Forest, Culbin Section*, Forestry Commission. |
| SCOTT-MONTCRIEFF, W.G. (Ed). | 1905 | Records of the Proceedings of the Justiciary Court, Edinburgh. 1661–1668. 2, 61. (21 Nov. 1671). |
| SHAW, L. | 1775 | *The History of the Province of Moray*, Edinburgh. |
| SHAW, L. | 1827 | *The History of the Province of Moray*, 2nd Edition, Edinburgh. |
| SINCLAIR, J. (Ed). | 1799 | *The Statistical Account of Scotland 1791–1799*, Edinburgh. |
| SISSONS, J.B. | 1963 | Scottish Raised Shoreline Heights with particular reference to the Forth Valley, *Geogr. Ann. Stockh.*, 45, 180–85. |
| SISSONS, J.B. | 1981 | Late Glacial Marine Erosion and a Jökulhlaup deposit in the Beauly Firth, *Scott. J. Geol.* 17, (1), 7–19. |
| STEERS, J.A. | 1937 | The Culbin Sands and Burghead Bay, *Geogr. Jl.* 90, 498. |
| STEERS, J.A. | 1969 | *The Sea Coast*, 4th Edition, London. |

STEERS, J.A.  1973  *The Coastline of Scotland*, Cambridge.

STEVEN, H.M.  1936  The Afforestation of the Culbin Sands, *The Scottish Field*, 67, 34.

STEWART, E.J.A. &  1923  The Vegetation of the Culbin Sands, *Bot.*
PATTON, D.  *Exch.* Cl. 7, 253.

ST JOHN, C.  1846  The Sandhills of Morayshire: in *Short Sketches of the Wild Sports and Natural History of the Highlands*, London.

ST JOHN, C.  1863  *Natural History and Sport in Moray*, Edinburgh.

SUGDEN, D.E. &  1976  *Glaciers and Landscape*, Edward Arnold.
JOHN, B.S.

SYMON, J.A.  1959  *Scottish Farming Past and Present*, Edinburgh.

SYNGE, F.M.  1956  Glaciation of Northeast Scotland, *Scot. Geogr. Mag.* 72, 129–43.

SYNGE, F.M.  1977  Land and Sea Level Changes during the waning of the last Regional Ice Sheet in the Vicinity of Inverness in Gill, G. (Ed). *The Moray Firth Area: Geological Studies*, Inverness. 83.

TAYLER, A. &  1914  *The Book of the Duffs*, Edinburgh.
TAYLER, H. (Eds).

TREGIDO, D.A.  1982  *Mapping and Analysis of Buried Soils of Culbin Forest, Morayshire*, Unpublished Thesis, University of Lancaster.

WALKER, A.D. et al.  1974  Soil Map, Sheet 84 (Nairn) and part of 94 (Cromarty), *Soil Survey of Scotland*, Aberdeen. Macaulay Institute for Soil Research.

WALKER, I.C.  1966  The Counties of Nairnshire, Moray and Banffshire in the Bronze Age, *Proc. Soc. Ant. Scot.* 98 (1964–66), 76.

WALLACE, T.D.  1880  The Geology of Rathven and Enzie, *Trans Inverness Sc. Soc. and Field Club*, 1, 300–309.

WALLACE, T.D.  1883  Shells in Glacial Clay at Fort George, Inverness-shire, *Trans. Edin. Geol. Soc.* 4, 143.

WALLACE, T.D.  1896  Recent Geological Changes and the Culbin Sands, *Trans. Inverness Sc. Soc. and Field Club*, 5, 105.

WALSH, M.  1937  *And No Quarter*, Chambers.

WALTON, J.  1957  Cruck-framed Buildings in Scotland, *Gwerin*, 1, 109–22.

WATSON, J. &  1868  The Ever-shifting Sands of Culbin: in
WATSON, W.  *Morayshire Described*, Elgin.

WEBSTER, M. McC.  1968  *Check List of the Flora of the Culbin State Forest*, Elgin.

WEBSTER, M. McC.     1978     *Flora of Moray, Nairn and East Inverness*, Aberdeen University Press.

WHITE, I.     1979     *Agriculture and Society in 17th Century Scotland*, Edinburgh.

WILLIS, D.P.     1986     *Sand and Silence—Lost Villages of the North*, Centre for Scottish Studies, University of Aberdeen.

WRIGHT, T.W.     1955     Profile Development in the Sand Dunes of Culin Forest, Morayshire: (1) Physical Properties. *Jl. Soil Sc.* 6, 270–83.

WRIGHT, T.W.     1956     Profile Development in the Sand Dunes of Culbin Forest, Morayshire: (2) Chemical Properties. *Jl. Soil Sc.* 7, 33–42.

YOUNG, A.     1970     Culbin Sands: in Scott, T. (Ed). *The Penguin Book of Scottish Verse*, 422.

YOUNG, R.     1871     *The Parish of Spynie*, Elgin.

YOUNG, R.     1879     *Annals of the Parish and Burgh of Elgin*, Elgin.

## MORAY SCHOOLS EDUCATIONAL MATERIAL

McKAY, J.                              *The Culbin Story.*
O'BRIEN, R.M.G. &                      *The Culbin Trail—A Teacher's Guide.*
McKAY, J.
McKAY, J.                              *Culbin—Development of Topics.*
O'BRIEN, R.M.G. &                      *Wind and Wave. Unit 1.*
McKAY, J.
McKAY, J. &                            *Reclaiming the Desert. Unit 2.*
O'BRIEN, R.M.G.

                                       CULBIN KEYS:
—                                      *A Guide to the Common Shells of the Culbin
                                       and Findhorn Areas.*
—                                      *A Guide to the Common Flowers of the Culbin
                                       and Findhorn Areas.*
—                                      *A Guide to the Common Mosses, Lichens,
                                       Shrubs and Coniferous Trees of the Culbin
                                       Forest.*
MILLS, P.R. & O'BRIEN,                 *Findhorn Outdoor Centre—Biological Field
R.M.G. (Eds).                          Studies.*
—                                      *Geographical Fieldwork Exercises—Find-
                                       horn.*

# APPENDIX 1

*LIST OF MAPS OF THE MORAY AREA WHICH INCLUDE CULBIN*

| | | |
|---|---|---|
| 1590 | Timothy Pont | Manuscript Map of Western Moray. NLS. G23, 25, Parts of Moray: G22 (River Findhorn). |
| 1654 | J. Blaeu | Moravia Scotia provinca ex Timothy Pont scedis descripta et actua per Robert Gordonium a Strathloch. |
| 1685 | Capt. Grenville Collins | Ms. of 'The Firth of Moray' for Great Britain's Coasting Pilot, 1693. |
| 1714 | Herman Moll | The North Part of Great Britain called Scotland. |
| 1718 | Herman Moll | A new and correct Map of Scotland and the Isles. |
| 1725 | Herman Moll | The Shires of Murray and Nairn in 'Scotland divided into its Shires'. |
| 1730 | Avery | The Moray Coast. (For York Buildings Company). |
| 1749 | W. Anderson | Plan of His Grace The Duke of Gordon and Sir Robert Gordon's Estate and Mosses in the west end of the Parish of Duffus. (RHP 2016). |
| 1755 | General Roy | Moray and Nairn. (Military Map). (B. Mus. K.48.256 Sheet 21). |
| 1758 | Peter May | A Survey of the River Findhorn. (With descriptive text). |
| 1764 | Peter May | The Watercourse leading to the Miln of West Grange with the Sogers Burn and such other contiguous fields and places. (RHP 32). |
| 1765 | Peter May | A Plan of the River Findhorn from the Sluy Pool downwards to the River Mouth. (RHP 10). |
| 1770 | George Brown | Plan of Brodie Estates. Brodie Castle. |
| 1773 | Alex. Taylor | Detailed Plan of the Runrig Lands in the west end of the Parish of Duffus. (RHP 2004). |
| 1776 | | Plan of the Lands of Moy. Moray District Record Office: DGS P1. |
| 1783 | Hugh Kinnaird | Map of the Loch of Spynie: in Mackintosh, 1928. |
| 1797 | Wm. Miller | The Province of Moray: in Grant & Leslie, 1798. |
| 1810 | George Brown | Map of Moray and Nairn Shires: in Leslie, 1811. |
| 1833 | | Plan of Part of Brodie Estates. |
| 1835 | | Moray Firth: Admiralty Survey. |
| 1858 | James Leslie | Findhorn Estuary. EP 33/8/1859. (RHP 510). |
| 1904 | | Ordnance Survey. |
| 1923 | A.G. Ogilvie | The Culbin Sand Dunes: in Ogilvie, 1923. |
| 1937 | Fisher & Balchin | The Culbin Sands and Burghead Bay: in Steers, 1937. |
| 1955 | | Ordnance Survey. |
| 1974 | | Ordnance Survey. |

APPENDIX 2

The Western Moray Coast from Blaeu's *Moravia*, 1654.

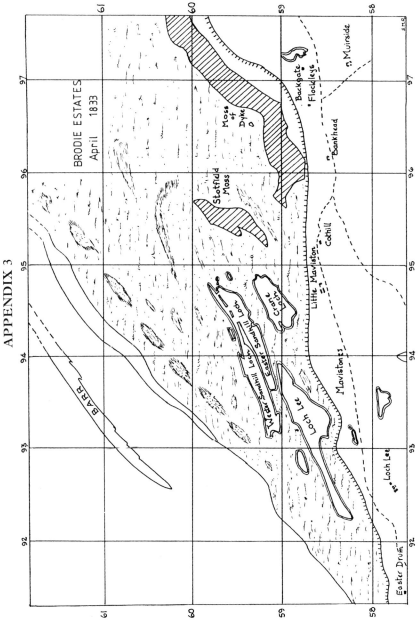

Lochs and mosses at the western end of Brodie Estates in 1833. (N.B. Grid superimposed without correction.)

# APPENDIX 4

## PEBBLE COUNTS FROM AREAS OF 2 SQUARE METRES ON SHINGLE RIDGES

|  | 1 | 2 | 3 | 4 | 5 | 6 | 7 | 8 |
|---|---|---|---|---|---|---|---|---|
| HORNBLENDE ANDESITE | 0 | 2 | 2 | 1 | 3 | 2 | 0 | 1 |
| BRECCIATED ANDESITE | 1 | 2 | 2 | 2 | 3 | 1 | 2 | 2 |
| OTHER ANDESITES | 2 | 1 | 0 | 5 | 1 | 2 | 4 | 1 |
| DACITE | 2 | 0 | 1 | 3 | 0 | 1 | 4 | 0 |
| RHYOLITE/RHYOLITIC TUFF | 0 | 6 | 4 | 5 | 2 | 3 | 2 | 2 |
| QUARTZ FELDSPAR PORPHYRY | 1 | 3 | 8 | 7 | 5 | 2 | 12 | 8 |
| "PORPHYRITE" | 1 | 2 | 0 | 5 | 3 | 2 | 14 | 4 |
| LAMPROPHYRE | 1 | 0 | 6 | 1 | 1 | 2 | 1 | 8 |
| FELSITE | 4 | 6 | 4 | 5 | 3 | 2 | 6 | 2 |
| GRANITE | 0 | 2 | 2 | 2 | 1 | 0 | 1 | 0 |
| MICROGRANITE | 18 | 15 | 6 | 13 | 2 | 46 | 30 | 16 |
| COARSE GNEISS | 0 | 9 | 14 | 1 | 0 | 0 | 0 | 0 |
| PSAMMITIC GNEISS | 242 | 609 | 510 | 543 | 517 | 700 | 494 | 592 |
| QUARTZITE | 48 | 85 | 80 | 47 | 41 | 22 | 274 | 90 |
| VEIN QUARTZ | 0 | 9 | 2 | 6 | 3 | 12 | 26 | 4 |
| METAMORPHIC GRIT | 2 | 4 | 0 | 1 | 11 | 20 | 4 | 22 |
| SCHIST | 0 | 0 | 0 | 0 | 0 | 0 | 0 | 10 |
| CHERT | 0 | 4 | 0 | 3 | 0 | 2 | 2 | 0 |
| FLINT | 0 | 0 | 0 | 1 | 0 | 0 | 4 | 0 |
| SANDSTONE | 332 | 2 | 4 | 0 | 4 | 46 | 0 | 4 |
| BRECCIA | 4 | 6 | 0 | 1 | 1 | 7 | 26 | 6 |
| JURASSIC SHALE | 1 | 0 | 0 | 0 | 0 | 1 | 1 | 0 |
|  | 659 | 767 | 645 | 652 | 601 | 871 | 907 | 772 |

1. Beach 500m west of Golf Club House, Nairn. (NH 861 568)
2. Centre of Old Bar. (NH 941 612)
3. Beach 500m west of Buckie Loch, Culbin. (NH 992 645)
4. Inland shingle ridges, Culbin Forest. (NH 992 626)
5. Beach north of Findhorn village. (NJ 043 647)
6. Beach below "90 Steps" quarry: 2.5km ENE HOPEMAN. (NJ 168 705)
7. W end modern storm beach shingle ridge: 3km SE Lossiemouth. (NJ 270 685)
8. Beach ca. 2.0km NW Garmouth. (NJ 320 664)

# APPENDIX 5

*FIELD EVIDENCE TO BE SATISFIED IN DEVELOPMENT SEQUENCE*

1. Deep, aligned, offshore channels which held core of Moray Firth Ice.
2. ENE-orientated features suggestive of ice-marginal drainage: marginal terraces, some of which have been interpreted as raised beaches. These traceable intermittently from Forres eastwards and include high level gravel deposits at Hopeman and Lossiemouth, and an apron round the Coltfield ridge (esker).
3. Marginal lake deposits. Dated marginal/terminal lake deposits in Banff Basin: shows sea level still low at 14,000 BP.
4. Spey gravels extend up to 10km offshore in a coarse fan and become finer and sandy eastwards for 70km. Links with Peacock's interpretation of Coastal Deposits: but of later date and probably result of catastrophic drainage of ice-dammed lake.
5. With rise of sea levels, these gravels were reworked westwards in longshore drift to form ridges blocking the exit of the Lossie and passed westwards to north of Covesea-Roseisle ridge.
6. Marine incursion into Spynie Depression and westwards. Traced through old loch beds and mosses, with confirmation from borehole logs.
7. Bedrock depth as noted in boreholes is considerable.
8. Peaty soils with some reed-swamp peat ca. 1.0 to 2.0m below O.D. in east end of Burghead Bay and under Kinloss.
9. Marine clays and estuarine silts with oysters in Burghead Bay. 8 & 9 have both been deposited on top of coarse rounded cobbles and boulders which from the amount of sandstone and chert have not travelled far. The source of these is most probably the Covesea-Roseisle Ridge.
10. Some 7.5m of marine-deposited pebbly sand covers 8 & 9.
11. This sand has a steady deposition rate—indicating a steady rise in sea level (Plate 5).
12. A shingle ridge system lies on the landward side of the modern beach and forms the tops of these deposits: probably laid down when sea level ca. 5.5m above present.
13. The width of the shingle ridge system indicates that most southerly ridge, the first to form, was driven landwards with the rising sea, then as sea level fell or oscillated other ridges were formed on its northern side: all indicating a plentiful supply of materials.
14. The "X" recurves of Steers (1937) on the most southerly ridge probably caused by breaks in the first bar as in the case of the present day Old Bar (fig. 6, p.14).

15. The bank cut by the entrance road to the Roseisle Picnic Area, (NJ 107 653) is formed of compact ?lake-bed deposits and is capped by an ancient soil. The 8.0m drop in level on its northern flank indicates truncation by wave- or later drainage channel-action.

16. Sections in the sand and gravel "cliff" flanking Burghead Bay show that the marine deposits were cut by later fresh water drainage channels near the mouths of the Millie and Bessie Burns. To the southwest of the latter stream, a stretch of peat 500m wide, overlies silt above high water mark in the "cliff". Recurving ridges in the picnic area suggest that a channel was running southwest from the Outlet/Millie Burn area with a spit growing across its mouth. This could have connected with the Bessie Burn channel. Other channels probably ran via Hempriggs—Hatton—Kinloss and also south of the Coltfield Ridge to south of Kinloss. Note the presence of oyster shells on the beach.

17. The deep peat at Lower Hempriggs and in Hatton Moss is connected to 16.

18. The maps of the various mosses and lochs in the parish of Duffus indicate the drainage pattern there.

19. At the Whiteinch smallholdings just southwest of Kinloss alluvial soil lies on silty clay deposited on top of thin shingle. This in turn is underlain by thin peat on clay. Silty clays and lenses of peat extend southwest as far as Forres where they were encountered in boreholes and trenches at the sewage works and the town bypass.

20. The presence of hard Moinian and igneous rocks which form 99% of the shingle along the beaches, where the only in situ rocks are sandstones, points to the origin of these being important.

21. A development sequence must allow for this shingle to cross river mouths and estuaries.

22. The completed sequence of events must not be out of line with any of the above features.

# APPENDIX 6

Map showing the spatial distribution of the key sites along Burghead Bay.

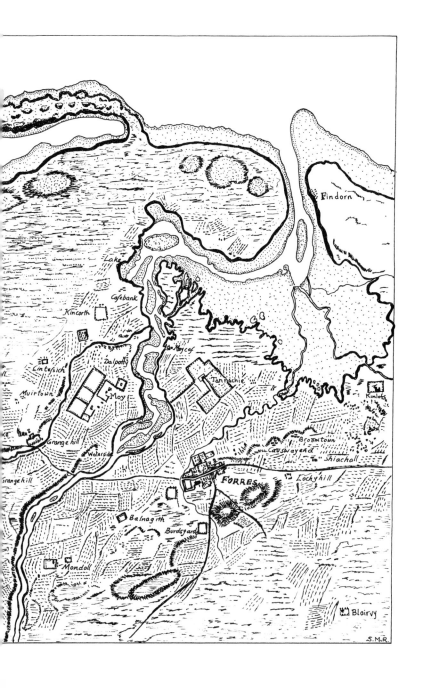

Findorn

Lake

Cosebank

Kincorth

Tar May cof

Dalpotty

Lintersich

Tannachie

Kinloss

Muirtoun

Moy

Broomtoun

Grangehill

Causwayend

Shiachall

Waterside

FORRES

Lochyhill

Grangehill

Balnagith

Burdsyard

Mondoll

Bloirvy

S.M.R.

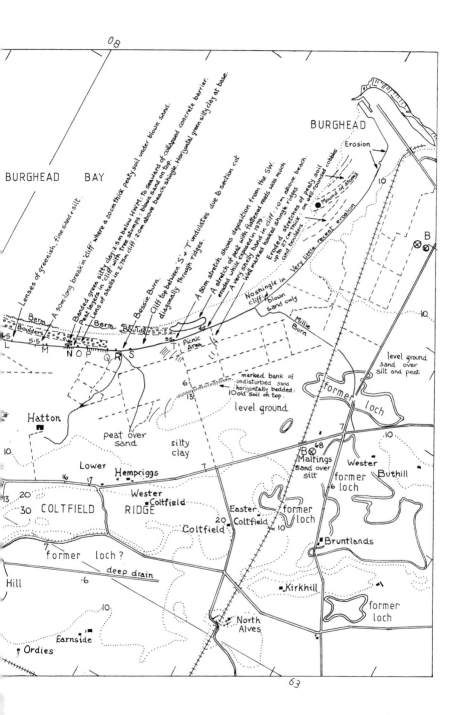

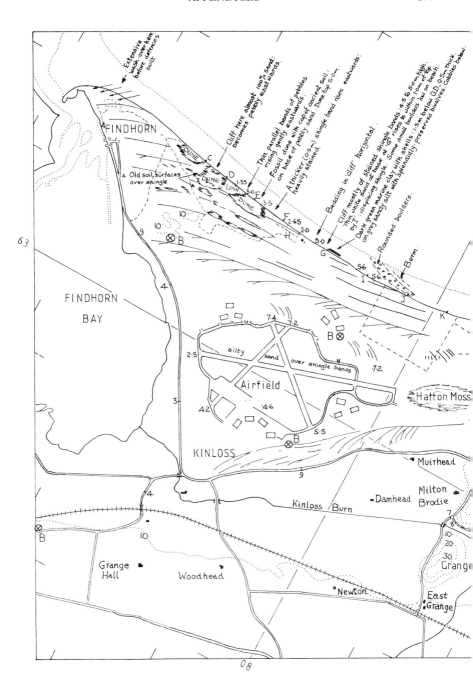

# APPENDIX 7
# BOREHOLES

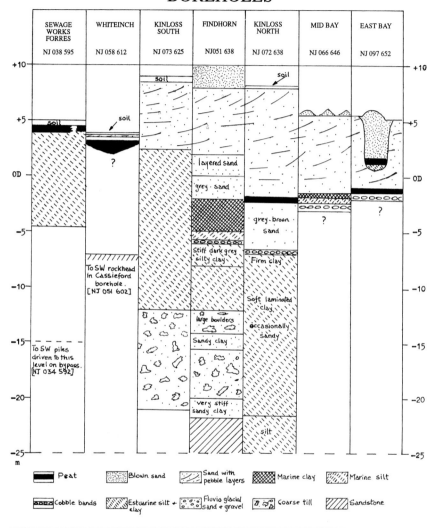

| SEWAGE WORKS FORRES | WHITEINCH | KINLOSS SOUTH | FINDHORN | KINLOSS NORTH | MID BAY | EAST BAY |
|---|---|---|---|---|---|---|
| NJ 038 595 | NJ 058 612 | NJ 073 625 | NJ051 638 | NJ 072 638 | NJ 066 646 | NJ 097 652 |

**Legend:**

Peat · Blown sand · Sand with pebble layers · Marine clay · Marine silt

Cobble bands · Estuarine silt + clay · Fluvio glacial sand + gravel · Coarse till · Sandstone

# APPENDIX 8

General Roy's map of Moray and Nairn, 1755.

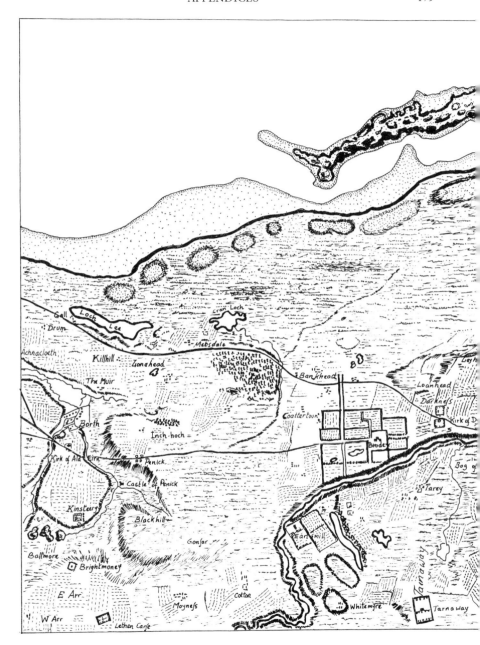

# APPENDIX 9

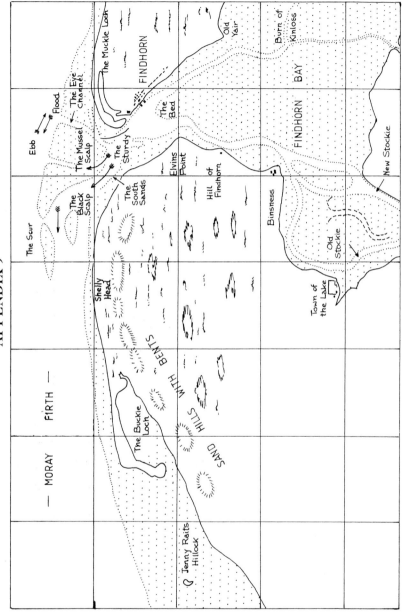

The Buckie Loch in 1858 from fishing dispute map by John Leslie.

## APPENDIX 10

# RENTALS FOR CULBIN ESTATE 1693 - AS QUOTED BY FRASER - MACKINTOSH

|  |  | MONEY £ | WHEAT | BEAR | OATS | MEAL |
|---|---|---|---|---|---|---|
| Sandifield | J. Dunbar | £200 | 40 bolls | 40 bolls | 40 bolls | 40 bolls |
| Culbin | W. Smith | £ 40 | 40 | 40 | 40 | 40 |
| | W. Maver | 40 | 40 | 40 | 40 | 40 |
| Middlebin | W. Falconer | 40 | 40 | 40 | 40 | 40 |
| | J. Dunbar | 200 | 40 | 40 | 40 | 40 |
| | G. Duncan | 200 | 40 | 40 | 40 | 40 |
| | A. Maver | 200 | 40 | 40 | 40 | 40 |
| Total | | £ 680 | 200 | 200 | 200 | 200 |
| Earnhill | D. Duncan | £ 200 | 40 | 40 | 40 | 40 |
| | A. Milne | 200 | 40 | 40 | 40 | 40 |
| Laik | R. Elgin | 200 | 40 | 40 | 40 | 40 |
| | A. Lauchlan | 200 | 40 | 40 | 40 | 40 |
| | A. Milne (Jr) | 200 | 40 | 40 | 40 | 40 |
| Total | | £ 800 | 160 | 160 | 160 | 160 |
| | R. Bluntach | 200 | 40 | 40 | 40 | 40 |
| | J. Jack | 200 | 40 | 40 | 40 | 40 |
| | J. Laughton | 200 | 40 | 40 | 40 | 40 |
| | J. Kynock | 200 | 40 | 40 | 40 | 40 |
| Total | | £ 800 | 160 | 160 | 160 | 160 |
| Grand Total | | £ 2720 | 640 | 640 | 640 | 640 |

## APPENDIX 11
## ABSTRACT OF THE RENT PAYMENTS & ARREARS
## OF THE LANDS OF CULBIN CROFT 1733
### The Victual Rent being stated at 8.5 merks per boll

| | TENANTS NAME | VICTUAL RENT B F P L | MONEY RENT £ : s : d | YARN HEERS | CAPONS | REEK HENS | POULTRY | LOADS OF PEAT |
|---|---|---|---|---|---|---|---|---|
| LAIK | William Falconer | 9 2 - - | | 6 | 4.5 | 2 | - | 13 |
| | James Duncan | 9 2 - - | | 6 | 4.5 | 2 | - | 13 |
| | David Maver | 10 2 2 - | | 6 | 5 | 2 | - | 15 |
| | Robert Duncan | 2 1 2 - | | 0 | 2.5 | 2 | - | 3 |
| | James Kerr, now | 16 - - - | 5 : 6 : 8 | 12 | 6 | 8 | - | 20 |
| | John Bell | | | | | | | |
| DELPOTTIE | John Kynack | 9 1 1 2 | 3 : 6 : 8 | 6.5 | 4 | 6 | - | 10 |
| | William McFail | 1 2 - - | | 1.5 | 1.5 | 0 | - | 4 |
| | Findlay Smith for | - 2 - - | | 0 | 0.5 | 0 | - | 2 |
| | Margaret Innes | | | | | | | |
| | John Nicol | - - - - | 5 : 10 : 0 | 0 | 0 | 2 | 6 | 0 |
| | Robert Malcom | 4 2 2 2 | 2 : 13 : 4 | 3 | 3 | 4 | - | 5 |
| | John Duff late of Culbin | 3 3 - - | | | | - | - | - |
| | James Grant for Earnhill | 22 - - - | 11 : 1 : 4 | | | - | - | - |
| | and for Mill of Delpottie | 11 - - - <br> +9B bere meal <br> +1B 2F flour | | | | - | - | - |
| | TOTALS | 100 3 - - | 27 : 18 : 0 | 41 | 31.5 | 28 | 6 | 85 |
| | LESS MINISTER'S STIPEND | 17 - 3 2 | 5 : 15 : 4 | | | | | |
| | | 83 2 - 2 | £22 : 2 : 8 Scots. | | | | | |

# APPENDIX 12

## OLD SCOTTISH LAND MEASURES

1 Scots Acre = 1.26 English Acres
1 Rig = 0.25 Scots Acre
1 Dale = 2 Rigs
1 Oxgang = 13 Scots Acres
8 Oxgangs = 104 Scots Acres
= 1 Ploughgate (Plough)
1 Davoch = 4 Ploughgates
1/2 Davoch = The usual size of a glebe
(1 Hectare = 1.96 Scots Acres)

*Measurement by Rent*
1 Ploughgate = 1 Merkland
= (1 merk = 13/4d Scots)
1/2 Ploughgate = 6/8d land
1/4 Ploughgate = 3/4d land

APPENDIX 13

# THE MURRAYS OF CULBIN : THE LINK
# WITH THE MORMAERS OF MORAY

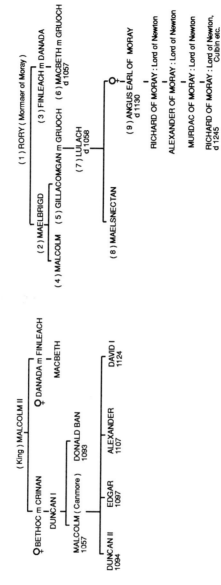

( 1 ) RORY ( Mormaer of Moray )

( 2 ) MAELBRIGD     ( 3 ) FINLEACH m DANADA

( 4 ) MALCOLM     ( 5 ) GILLACOMGAN m GRUOCH     ( 6 ) MACBETH m GRUOCH
d 1057

( 7 ) LULACH
d 1058

( 8 ) MAELSNECTAN

( 9 ) ANGUS EARL OF MORAY
d 1130

RICHARD OF MORAY : Lord of Newton

ALEXANDER OF MORAY : Lord of Newton

MURDAC OF MORAY : Lord of Newton

RICHARD OF MORAY : Lord of Newton,
d 1245                                        Culbin etc.

( King ) MALCOLM II

BETHOC m CRINAN     DANADA m FINLEACH

DUNCAN I     MACBETH

MALCOLM ( Canmore )     DONALD BAN
1057                            1093

ALEXANDER     DAVID I
1107                1124

DUNCAN II     EDGAR
1094              1097

King Malcolm II had two daughters, Bethoc and Danada. The succession of
the two Mormaers of Moray was strictly according to the laws of Tanistry : in
this case : father to son : son to brother : uncle to nephew : cousin to cousin.
Macbeth was slightly younger than his cousin Duncan & by these laws had
equal right to the throne, but Duncan had been chosen by his grandfather as
heir. Macbeth slew Duncan in 1040, and Crinan in 1045 and became " king ".
He married Gruoch, widow of Gillacomgan and on his death in 1057 was
succeeded by his step - son Lulach. Angus, the last Mormaer and Earl of
Moray was Lulach's grandson.

## APPENDIX 14
# THE GENEALOGY OF THE MURRAYS OF CULBIN
after D. Murray Rose ( 1900, 1925 )

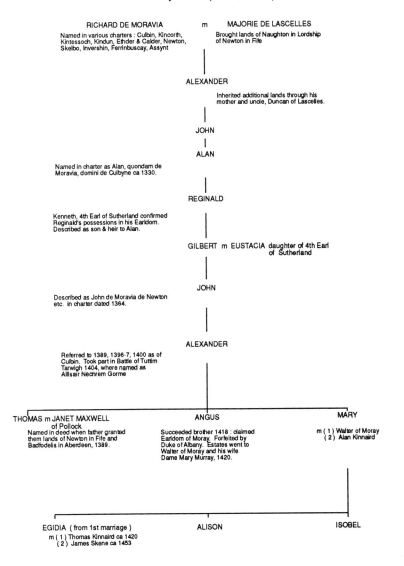

RICHARD DE MORAVIA    m    MAJORIE DE LASCELLES

Named in various charters : Culbin, Kincorth,    Brought lands of Naughton in Lordship
Kintessoch, Kindun, Ethder & Calder, Newton,    of Newton in Fife
Skelbo, Invershin, Ferrinbuscay, Assynt

ALEXANDER

Inherited additional lands through his
mother and uncle, Duncan of Lascelles.

JOHN

ALAN

Named in charter as Alan, quondam de
Moravia, domini de Culbyne ca 1330.

REGINALD

Kenneth, 4th Earl of Sutherland confirmed
Reginald's possessions in his Earldom.
Described as son & heir to Alan.

GILBERT  m  EUSTACIA  daughter of 4th Earl
of Sutherland

JOHN

Described as John de Moravia de Newton
etc. in charter dated 1364.

ALEXANDER

Referred to 1389, 1396-7, 1400 as of
Culbin. Took part in Battle of Tuttim
Tarwigh 1404, where named as
Allister Nechrem Gorme

THOMAS  m  JANET MAXWELL        ANGUS          MARY
of Pollock
Named in deed when father granted      Succeeded brother 1418 : claimed    m ( 1 ) Walter of Moray
them lands of Newton in Fife and      Earldom of Moray.  Forfeited by       ( 2 ) Alan Kinnaird
Badfodelis in Aberdeen, 1389.         Duke of Albany.  Estates went to
Walter of Moray and his wife
Dame Mary Murray, 1420.

EGIDIA ( from 1st marriage )        ALISON          ISOBEL
m ( 1 ) Thomas Kinnaird ca 1420
( 2 ) James Skene ca 1453

## APPENDIX 15

# THE KINNAIRDS OF CULBIN

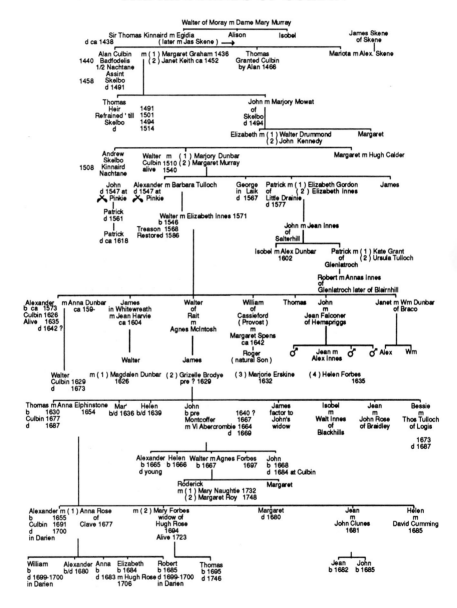

# APPENDIX 16

*OLD DOCUMENTS DEALING WITH THE BARONY OF CULBIN*

NOTE: Some of these documents are no longer available for study, but are referred to and/or have been studied by various researchers: mainly: C. Fraser Mackintosh, E. Dunbar Dunbar and the Rev. J.G. Murray. They are therefore treated as being factual.

| Date | REFERENCE | SUMMARY OF DOCUMENT ETC. |
|---|---|---|
| 1236 | Registrum Episc. Moraviensis p.464 | Richard de Moravia feued Great Kincorth and Little Kyntessoch. |
| 1330 | Gordon (1813) | Sir Robert Gordon here dates Gilbert's marriage to Eustacia of Sutherland. |
| 1364 | Reg. Mag. Sig. Vol.1 No.186 | John de Moravia de Newton etc. recorded in charter. |
| 1389 | BATTEN (1877) p.92 | Alexander de Moravia de Coulbin stood as co-security for Lord Alexander, Earl of Buchan and Lord of Ross (The Wolf) not to mistreat the Lady Ross. |
| 1389 | Antiquities of the Shires of Aberdeen & Banff p.262 | Thomas Murray of Culbyne and his wife Janet Maxwell, daughter of Sir John Maxwell (4th) of Pollock were granted a charter of lands in the Lordship of Newton in Fife, with others in Aberdeenshire-Badfodall. The deed, involving his father Alexander de Moravia de Culbyne, was witnessed by Thomas, "his son and heir". |
| 1390 | Memoirs of the Maxwells of Pollock, p.15 | Here Fraser dates this charter as between 1390 and 1406. |
| 1393 | Reg. Mag. Sig. Vol.I app 2. 1705 | In Robertson's Index of Charters the above charter is placed in a roll whose dated charters bear the date 1393. |
| 1391 | F. Mackintosh p.313 | Alexander Moray of Culbin granted a charter in the county of Forfar. |
| 1396 | Antiquities of the Shires of Aberdeen & Banff p.263 | Alexander de Moravia de Colbyn was present at an Inquisition in Feb. 1396–7. |
| 1400 | Gordon (1813) | Alexander Morray of Culbin (also called Allister Neschrem Gorme) was witness to a charter and named as taking part in Battle of Tuttim Tarwigh. |

| | |
|---|---|
| 1404 The History of the Province of Cat. | The Rev. Angus Mackay gives the date of this battle as 1404. |
| 1427 op.cit. p.98 | Mackay states Angus Moray of Culbin was among the northern notables apprehended by James I in Inverness in 1427 and later released. |
| 1429 Reg. Mag. Sig. Vol.II No.149 | Angus Moray rewarded by James I for capture of Thomas MacNeil with the grant of lands in Ross & Sutherland. |
| 1433 History of the Province of Cat. p.101 | Mackay states Angus Moray died at the Battle of Drum nan Coup in 1433. |
| 1436–SRO GD 48/30.2 1437 | Rossie Priory Manuscripts list James I receiving resignation by Thomas Kinnaird and his wife Egidia of the lands of Culbin, 1/2 Nachtane, 1/2 Badfodelis and Assynt, and sasine thereof to Alan their son and heir. |
| 1438 Antiquities of the Shires of Aberdeen & Banff p.266 | On 12th May Egidia issued a revocation of the above resignation, stating that it related to the marriage being contracted between Alan and Margaret, daughter of the Lord Grahme: asserting that the agreement had been forced on her by her husband, now dead. |
| 1440 op.cit. p.267 &Abb. Reg. Mag. Sig. IV No.16 | Here the trouble appears to have been resolved by the grant of the lands to Alan, subject to his mother's life-rent of Culbin, and other reservations. |
| 1449 F. Mackintosh p.313 | Charter of renunciation by Thomas Tarrel of lands in the Lordship of Skibo in favour of "The honourable Lady Egidia Moray of Culbin", dated 16 Oct. 1449. |
| 1453 SRO EX GD 125/6 | Egidia, having married James Skene of Skene granted him a share of her life-rent of Skelbo and of 1/2 Nachtane. He and his son guaranteed not to put claim to the lands belonging to Egidia and which were to pass to Alaine. The son Alexander also received some life rents. |
| 1458 Memorials of the Family of Skene pp.17 & 21 | In 1438 Mariota, Alan Kinnaird's sister married Alexander Skene son of James Skene of Skene. In 1453 Egidia married her daughter's father in law, and now transfers the estate of Skelbo to Alan. |
| 1466 J.G. Murray p.6 | Alan granted to his brother Thomas, their mother being then alive, and with her consent, the lands and barony of Culbin, Delputtie, Easterbin, Muirtown and Aikenhead, reserving to himself in life rent the Girseyards: and to Egidia the life rent of all the lands. |
| 1478 J.G. Murray p.7 | Alan Kinnaird and Janet Keith, his wife, received a royal charter under the "white wax" of the barony of Culbin 25 Feb. 1478. |

| | |
|---|---|
| 1493 F. Mackintosh p.314 | Thomas Kinnaird infeft in the castle and lands of Skibo. 25 Aug. 1493 in Inverness. |
| 1501 J.G. Murray p.8 | Andrew, Lord Gray, held the baronies of Kinnaird, Culbin and Nachtane while they were in the King's hands during the period of non-entry of Thomas. For this Lord Grey received a compensation of £333. 6s. 8d. when Thomas was served heir to his father on 23 Jan. 1501. |
| 1506 SRO GD 248/32/5.1 | Thomas sold the lands of Over and Nether Tillieglens in Edinkillie parish while one third of the Mains of Culbin, formerly belonging to Elizabeth Kynnard and Margaret Kynnard "daughters of my brother John" was resigned into his hands. Dated in "dunde" 23 Feb. 1506. |
| 1507 op.cit. & J.G. Murray p.8 | Thomas disponed to John Calder, presenter of Rosse, probably in warrandice of the above transaction the one third of the Mains of Culbin. One of the witnesses thereto is given as Andrew Kynnard of Selbo, his son and heir. |
| 1508 J.G. Murray p.8 | Andrew Kynnaird received sasine of Skelbo and inherited the estates of Skelbo, Kinnaird and Nachtane, when Thomas died in 1514. |
| 1510 J.G. Murray p.9 | Walter Kinnaird, second son of Thomas, received from his father on 12 Sept. 1510, a resignation in his favour of "all and haill the barony of Culbin with the teinds and tenantry of the same and 100 merks annually out of any lands of the Lordship of Skelbo". |
| 1511 J.G. Murray p.10 | Walter Kinnaird married Marjory Dunbar, probably in 1511, as on the 9th Jan. of that year the King confirmed to him and her in conjunct fee, the lands of Delpottine with the mill and multures thereof. |
| 1529 Fraser (1892) p.514 | William Sutherland of Duffus, who had held a wadset on the lands of Skelbo against a loan of 1500 merks to John Kinnaird son and heir to Andrew, acquired these lands in 1529. |
| 1538 RS 29/6 p.36 of 1 June 1725 | Reference to Alexander, Prior of Pluscarden, having an agreement with Walter Kinnaird and a James Learmonth of Darsey re. rights on peats and grazing of cattle in the mosses of Logie and Rochecarse conforming to a contract signed in Edinburgh 17 March, 1538. |
| 1538? RS 29/3 p.117 line 50 | Reference in this sasine (Baillie Duff of Inverness in 1692) to original charters on fishing rights "... had rights be progres from Robert, Bishop of Orkney and Abbot of Kinloss with consent of his convent by charter dated the..... day of.....yeirs and thereafter |

from Walter, Abbot of Kinloss with consent of his convent conform to this and their charter granted thereto dated the first day of September 1581 yeirs confirmed by King James of blessed memory be his highnes charter under the greit seall of Scotland dated the tenth day of October 1586 and after which confirmed in the person of Walter Kinnaird of Culbin under the great seall upon the twentie day of June 1642 yeirs". See also entry under 1631 re. fishing charter.

| | |
|---|---|
| 1539 Reg. Sec. Sig. Vol.II 3417 | The four Kinnaird brothers Alexander, George, Patrick and James are listed in a precept dated 29 Feb. 1539. |
| 1547 Registrum Episc. Moraviensis p.421 | 24 Jan 1547, Patrick Kinnaird and his spouse Elizabeth Gordon granted a charter by Patrick Hepburn (454) Carta feodifirmae Salterhill alias Little Drainie and (457) Mid Tullibardin, Gedloch, Glenlatroquhy and Blairnahay. |
| 1567 Acta Parliamentorum: Jacobi VI | 19–20 Dec 1567, Walter Kinnaird along with his ? Cousins Hepburne, Jacob Innes of Drainie and Thomas Tulloch of Fleurs accused of treason. |
| 1570 J.G. Murray p.12 | Walter Kinnaird granted the lands of Laik to his uncle Patrick. |
| 1571 op. cit. | Walter Kinnaird and his newly married wife, Elizabeth Innes, Received from the Bishop of Moray, Patrick Hepburn, a 19 years tack of the teindscheaves of his lands of Culbin, Muirtown and Laik, for the annual payment of £12. 6s. 8d. |
| 1588 Moray Archives 2BF A52/1/69 | Mention that John Kinnaird, son of Patrick Kynnard, burgess of Forres, was tacksman of "the schireffis stell and corfhows of Dyk". |
| 1602 Session Minute SRO CHZ/145/2 | In the minutes of the Elgin Kirk Session of April 1602, James Kinnaird was described as second son lawful to Walter Kinnaird of Culbin. |
| 1610 J.G. Murray p.13 | Walter Kinnaird signed a bond imposed on him not to harm Samuel Falconer of Kincorth. |
| 1620 J.G. Murray p.16 | Walter Kinnaird Junior absolved by Lords of Session in dispute over fishings with Robert Dunbar of Easterbin on whose lands Walter Kinnaird held a wadset. |
| 1625 RS 28/3 p.18 | Robert Dunbar of Easterbin paid 2500 merks to Walter Kinnaird, son of Walter Kinnaird of Culbin, in redemption of his two ploughs land of Easterbin. |
| 1626 J.G. Murray p.19 | Alexander Kinnaird was served heir to his father Walter on 4th April 1626, in the lands of Culbin viz..... etc. |
| 1626 SRO GD 245/95/2/1 | A charter granted by Alexander Kinnaird to his son |

Walter refers to a marriage contract dated 14th June 1626, between Walter and Magdalene Dunbar, daughter of Martin Dunbar of Grangehill.

1627 RS 28/3 p.101B  Alexander Kinnaird gets superiority of Cowbin on payment of £40, the right having been in crown hands for one year.

1629 RS 28/3 pp.223–225B  Walter Kinnaird and his wife Grisselle Brodye get ? feudal tenancy of lands of Cowbin etc. while Walter's parents were still alive. Alexander gets life rent etc. of Laik and Sandifield while Elizabeth Innes (grandmother) gets an annuity of 24 bolls victuals. Alexander also reserves the Manse of the Chapel of St Ninian.

1631 RS 28/3 p.316B & J.G. Murray p.19  Walter Kinnaird received from James Spens of Alves, Kirktown, a charter of the salmon fishings on the water of Findhorn, called the Common, alias the Sheriffstell on the west side of the river..... (which charter received the Royal confirmation in 1642. Sasine dated 15 Sept. 1631.

1632 RS 28/3 pp.337–338  Marjorie Erskine named as "future spouse" of Walter Kinnaird is granted life rent of the lands of Cowbin etc., with permission of Walter's father, Alex.

1635 RS 28/4 p.59B  12th Jan. Helen Forbes received sasine on lands of Culbin with permission of Walter's father, Alex. She is referred to as "nunc spouse honorabilis vir Walter Kinnaird de Cowbin".

1635 RS 28/4 p.62  6 April, 1635 Samuel Falconer of Kincorth and his son William Falconer, minister of Dyke received from Walter Kinnaird hereditary sasine of the Manse of the Chapel of St. Ninian.

1642 F. Mackintosh p.315  On 20th June Walter Kinnaird received a charter from Charles I to the estate of Culbin. This included confirmation of the fishing rights mentioned in 1631.

1644 RS 28/4 p.341  On 19 March 1644, Helen Forbes receives sasine of life rent to part of Culbin estate. This was a re-affirmation of the sasine granted in 1635, when she married Walter Kinnaird (who, after getting the 1642 charter was now the feudal superior).

1649 RS 28/5 p.14  27th Dec. 1649, Walter Kinnaird had a sasine to the lands of Erneside and Ordies, of which the proprietor was William Cumming.

1650 RS 28/5 p.85 of 1652 refers  4th Jan. 1650, letter comprysing Wm Chalmer vs Sir Alexander Innes with Walter Kinnaird as his cautioner, for wrongfully dispossessing Wm. Chalmer from the lands of Sherestoun. Sued for 7500 merks Kinnaird formally denounced by land

| | |
|---|---|
| | messenger and the total sum sought was 9950 merks against the lands and baronie of Cowbin. |
| 1651 RS 28/5 p.57B | 28 April 1651, Walter Kinnaird had heritable sasine on Earnside and Ordies. |
| 1651 RS 28/5 p.60 | 17 May 1651, Walter Kinnaird paid 3500 merks to Lt. Col. Lachlan Ross as redemption of the lands of Earnside and Ordies—on the loan the Lt. Col. had made to Wm. Cumming. |
| 1652 RS 28/5 p.72 | Judgement of Commissioners on Wm. Chalmer versus Walter Kinnaird from 1650. |
| 1652 RS 28/5 p.84 | Walter Kinnaird obtained charter of lands of Clackmarres with teindschiefs from Sir Alexander Innes of Cockstown. 7th Nov. '52 (redeemable). |
| 1652 RS 28/5 p.85 | Walter Kinnaird, as cautioner to Sir Alex. Innes had been accused with the latter of unjustly dispossessing Walter Chalmer and his wife of the town and lands of Sherestoun in the parish of St Andrews about 1647. Walter Kinnaird gives lands of Clackmarras to Wm. Chalmer in (part) payment of settlement. |
| 1653 RS 28/5 p.130 | Walter Kinnaird gives life rent of Mains of Cowbin, Middlebin, Laik and Sandifield to Anna Elphinstoun on her marriage to his eldest son Thomas on 7th May '53. |
| 1655 RS 28/5 p.190 | 5th June '55, Walter Kinnaird raises charter of apprysing on heritable saisine held on lands of Erneside. This now covers additional lands of Incheberie, Elljey, Ordechuisse and all and haill the curreche cowbill streams and salmond fishing of the waters of the Spey pertining to Wm. Cumming of Erneside. All and haill the town and lands of meikle Phorpe with the pertinents thereof called Craigroye, Thomnamoune, Aulduschak with the mill of Phorpe etc.—repayable/redeemable over 7 years. |
| 1660 RS 28/6 p.66 | 22nd Mar. '60. Walter Kinnaird had at one time (Date? presumably on the death of his cousin) come into possession of the lands of Braco and its pendicle Paulruggatie and he now sells them to Johne Falconer of Tulloch who was buying up land in the area at the time. (Braco and Over and Nether Blairie were owned as one unit up to 1581). Walter's aunt Janet had married Wm. Dunbar of Braco Ca 1610. |
| 1660 RS 28/6 p.87 | Walter Kinnaird obtained saisine on parts of the lands of Longmoregone in life rent for himself and in free for his second son John (who was later to marry Violet Abercrombie of Birkenbog). |
| 1664 RS 17/1 p.244 | Walter Kinnaird rents lands of Ordinghuis from Sir |

| | | |
|---|---|---|
| | | Alex. Abercrombie of Birkenbog at an annual rent of £180. |
| 1667 | The Family of Abercromby p.78 | 27 July. John Kinnaird and his wife received heritable disposition of the lands of Montcoffer, Carskie and inverichnie from his father-in-law, Sir Alex. Abercromby. |
| 1667 | RS 29/2 p.42 | 26th Dec. '67 Walter Kinnaird rents out fishing of his "Easter Stell" at a rent of 1000 merks and 4 barrells of salmon to John Dawson of Findhorn. |
| 1669 | RS 29/2 p.85 B | Walter Kinnaird grants heritable rights of the fishings of his Easter and Wester Stells to Johne Dawson on a wadset of 2000 merks. 1677 refers. |
| 1671 | Justiciary Proceedings Edinburgh | Thomas Kinnaird, younger, of Cowbin accused of slaughter. The case later deserted on "mistake". |
| 1673 | RS 29/2 p.237 B | Patrick Cumming of Erneside pays off his father's debts of 3050 merks owed to Walter Kinnaird and regains possession of Erneside etc. 25th Mar. '73. |
| 1673 | RS 29/2 p.244 B | On 26th Mar. Wm. Dunbar of Kintessack got from Walter Kinnaird a sasine of the toun and lands of Delpottie and Earnhill with a garden called Netherboll along with the Mill of Delpottie with thirlage, multures etc. in a redeemable wadset of 8500 merks. N.B. Laik not included. |
| 1673 | Brodie's Diary | Walter Kinnaird died on 24th October 1673. |
| 1676 | The Family of Abercromby p.80 | 9 Nov. After death of Vi Abercromby, the lands of Montcoffer, Carskie and Inverichnie were sold and the proceeds and life rent thereof were turned over to Thomas Kinnaird of Culbin and his eldest son Alexander as nearest relatives. The money was to be applied for the benefit of John Kinnaird's children. |
| 1677 | RS 29/2 p.425 B | Anne Rose, as spouse apparent to Alex. Kinnaird (jun) of Culbin, is granted life rent of Earnhill and Delpottie including the Mill of Delpottie etc. |
| 1677 | RS 29/3 p.6 | 16th Nov. '77, Thomas Kinnaird redeems the wadset on the Easter and Wester Stells held by Dawsone of Findhorn for 2000 merks. |
| 1677 | RS 29/3 p.10 B | 4th Dec. '77, Thomas Kinnaird gains succession to his father's estate after a four-year delay during which the rights lay in the hands of the court. This was possibly for the non-payment of feu duties. |
| 1682 | RS 29/3 p.116 | William Duff, baillie of Inverness, holds sasine (consolidated?) from Thomas Kinnaird dated 17 Apr. '82, on the 5 ploughs land of Binn, commonlie or of old called Middlebin at a yearlie rent of 90 bolls bere, the salmon fishing pertaining to the musle |

scalps of Cowbin, The Sheriffs or Common Stell, with the yearly rent for both stells of 30 barrells of salmon.

1682   RS 29/3 p.127   By 5th Sept. '82, the wadset held by Baillie Duff of Inverness increases to cover these listed above plus lands called the Maines, The Hill of Findhorn, the ferrie and ferrie coble on the Findhorn, the mussel scalp of Findhorn, the lands of Macrodder alias Mirrietoune, the lands of Aikenhead alias Rochcarse, Lands of Laik, Sandifeild and Dollaith alias Dilpottie with the miln of Dilpottie etc. The manse of the chapell and chapell of St Ninian: all against 25,000 merks. Adding that on non-payment of rental in the first part, eviction from part or all may follow at any time. The two precepts of sasine with charter following confirmed by his Majesty under the great seal, conform to the charter dated 26th July 1682. No further sasines to be taken by Wm. Duff on the said lands of Culbin.

1689   Proceedings of the Estates in Scotland   On 18th July 1689 "A Proclamation against the Viscount of Dundee, and other rebels now in arms" was issued in Edinburgh. It lists Kinnaird of Culbin and Innes of Coxton among the rebels, and declares their association to be high treason.

1691   F. Mackintosh p.316   Thomas Kinnaird died in 1691 and was succeeded by his son Alexander. This date conflicts with the date 1687 in Dyke Parish Register.

1691   J.G. Murray p.35   Alexander Kinnaird succeeded his father as Laird of Culbin.

1691   The Family of Abercromby p.78   6th May. A Judicial Enquiry was set up in Banff to look into the legality of the sale of the lands of Montcoffer etc. in 1676 while the eldest son (& heir) was still a minor.

1693   F. Mackintosh p.317 et seq.   The celebrated rental of Culbin is here quoted by F.M. for the year 1693. This presumably was presented with Baillie Duff's case to the Court of Session on 17th Feb. 1694. Enquiries to SRO point to its having been returned to the origin once presented, as there was no requirement for such additional documents to be preserved. The transcript of the case has been examined and no copy is filed with it. (F.M. was no doubt able to examine it along with the other materials he had obtained from Dunbar Dunbar).

1694   CS 29 Box 164 17 Feb. 1694   Baily Duff's litigation is intact in West Register House Edinburgh under this reference dated 4th Jan. 1694. (Copy of first part in file).

| | |
|---|---|
| 1694 SRO G125 Box 19 | William Kinnaird witnessed two deeds in Rose family papers in 1694 and 1696. In the latter he is described as "son to Alexander Kynnaird of Cowbin". |
| 1695 F. Mackintosh p.316 | A copy of Kinnaird's petition to Scottish Parliament for relief of cess and taxes as the best two parts of his estates had been covered by sand. |
| 1695 Acts of Parliament Scotland p.452 | Law passed forbidding the pulling of bent, broom or juniper off sand hills. It quotes the problems at Culbin. |
| 1695 op.cit. p.479 | This is the official version of the petition quoted by Fraser Mackintosh and there are some differences. A letter to SRO Edinburgh questioning whether or not the Lords Commissioners of the Treasury did in fact grant Alex. Kinnaird relief from cess, brought the answer to the effect that "Though the Lords may have discussed the matter, they certainly did not grant Alex. Kinnaird any money". |
| 1695 J.G. Murray p.39 | In direct conflict (?) with this statement, Murray states "After some deliberation the petition was remitted to the Lords Commissioners of the Treasury 'To do in the matter as they find just'." The latter body, having duly considered the facts of the case, decided to grant relief from cess on two thirds of the valued rental, but that payment must be made on the remaining third (£304. 12.9d Scots), from Martinmas next, and for so long as the said lands are overblown. Further approaches to different officials at SRO produced the statement that it was not unknown for clerks to forget to transfer data from their various notebooks to the official record, and that these notebooks should be consulted. |
| 1698 F. Mackintosh p.322 | From 1693 to 1697 processes of apprysing, adjudication, mails and duties and finally of ranking and sale were carried out. The papers did not show precisely what sum was paid at the judicial sale, but it appears Baillie Duff alone lost several thousand pounds Scots. The estate was purchased in the name of Alexander Duff, eldest son of Baillie Duff, styled "of Drummuir". A full copy of Alexander Kinnaird's disposition to Drummuir dated 27th July 1698 is given on pp.322–323. |
| 1698 J.G. Murray p.40 | It may be that Alex. Kinnaird's unsecured creditors had received some inkling of the ex gratia payment to him by Alex. Duff as there followed an appeal to parliament for protection. |

| 1698 | Acts of Parliament Scotland | Granted protection for Alex. Kinnaird of Culbin after three parts of his estates had been destroyed, and the remaining part sold to pay creditors. |
| 1702 | J.G. Murray p.40 & RS 29/4 p.110 | Alexander Duff received sasine on lands of Cowbin 17th May 1702. Registered on 10th August. Various other dates given. Most interesting is price paid by Duff at 1698 sale: £20,259.10. 6d Scots. |
| 1719 | RS 29/5 p.244B | Saisine of Alexander Dunbar of Grangehill refers to the grazing rights of Logie Moss and Rochecarse agreed by Alexander, Prior of Pluscardine, James Learmonth of Darsey and Walter Kinnaird of Cowbin. Dated Edinbught 17 Mar. 1538. Document in Latin. |
| 1725 | RS 29/6 pp.35B & 36 | Saisine of William Dunbar of Netherwaterside and Grange Green: mention of the grazing rights as in 1719. Text in English. |